Everyday Mathematics®

Student Math Journal 1

The University of Chicago
School Mathematics Project

A Division of The McGraw·Hill Companies

Columbus, Ohio
Chicago, Illinois

UCSMP Elementary Materials Component

Max Bell, Director

Authors

Max Bell
Jean Bell
John Bretzlauf*
Amy Dillard*
Robert Hartfield
Andy Isaacs*
James McBride, Director
Kathleen Pitvorec*
Peter Saecker

Technical Art

Diana Barrie*

*Second Edition only

Photo Credits

Phil Martin/Photography, Jack Demuth/Photography, Cover Credits: Sand, starfish, orange wedges, crystal/Bill Burlingham Photography, Photo Collage: Herman Adler Design Group

www.sra4kids.com

SRA/McGraw-Hill

A Division of The McGraw·Hill Companies

Send all inquiries to:
SRA/McGraw-Hill
P.O. BOX 812960
Chicago, IL 60681

Printed in the United States of America.

ISBN 1-57039-839-9

14 HS 07 06

Contents

Unit 1: Routines, Review, and Assessments

A note at the bottom of each journal page indicates when that page is first used. Some pages will be used again during the course of the year.

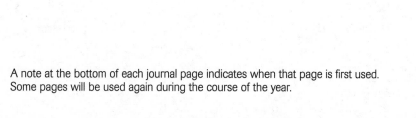

Unit 2: Adding and Subtracting Whole Numbers

Unit 3: Linear Measures and Area

Unit 4: Multiplication and Division

Unit 5: Place Value in Whole Numbers and Decimals

Unit 6: Geometry

Activity Sheets

A Numbers Hunt

Look for numbers in your classroom. Write the numbers in the table.
Look for numbers that you cannot "see" but you can find by counting
or measuring. Record these numbers, too.

Number	Unit (if there is one)	What does the number mean?	How did you find the number? (count, measure, another way?)
Example: 16	Crayons	Tells how many crayons are in a box	Number is on the box
Example: 30	Inches	Height of my desk	Measured my desk

Number-Grid Puzzles

1. Complete the grid.

541			544						550
551		553			556			559	
	562			565					570
			574			577			
581				585			588		
		593						599	
	602				606				
			614						620

Fill in the missing numbers.

2.

3.

4.

5.

6.

7.

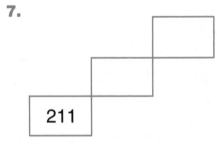

Make up your own puzzles. Ask someone to solve them.

8.

9.

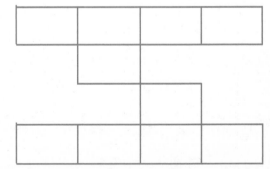

Looking up Information

Math Message

1. Turn to page 270 in your *Student Reference Book.*

   How many yards are there in 1 mile? _____ yards

Work with a partner. Use your *Student Reference Book* for Questions 3–6.

2. Write your partner's first name. _____

   Write your partner's last name. _____

3. Look up the word **circumference** in the Glossary. Copy the definition.

   _____

4. Read the essay "Tally Charts."

   a. Then solve the Check Your Understanding problems.

      Problem 1: _____

      Problem 2: _____

   b. Check your answers in the Answer Key.

   c. Describe what you did to find the essay.

   _____

   _____

5. Find the Measurement section. Which of the following units of length is about the same length as a person's height? _____

   a. yard   b. thumb   c. fathom   d. cubit   e. hand   f. foot

   On which page did you find the answer? _____

6. Look up the rules of the game *Less Than You!* Play the game with your partner.

Using Mathematical Tools

In Problems 1 and 2, record the time shown on the clocks. In Problem 3, draw the minute hand and the hour hand to show the time.

1.

2.

3.

6:10

_____   _____

Use your ruler.

4. Measure the line segment.   about _____ inches

    _____

5. Draw a line segment 10 centimeters long.

Use your calculator to do these problems.

6. 23,573 + 859 + 6,051 = _____   **7.** 20,748 − 8,967 = _____

8. 466 × 38 = _____   **9.** 1,978 ÷ 23 = _____

Use your Pattern-Block Template to draw the following shapes:

10. a rhombus   **11.** a hexagon   **12.** a trapezoid

Challenge

13. Which of the shapes in Problems 10–12 are quadrangles?

_____

Math Boxes 1.5

1. What is today's date?

_____

What will be the date in 6 days?

_____

What will be the date in 1 week?

_____

2. Fill in the missing numbers.

	174	
	205	

3. Write the number that is 10 more.

42 _____

160 _____

901 _____

Write the number that is 10 less.

59 _____

120 _____

4. Count back by 3s.

__42__ , _____ , _____ , __33__ ,

_____ , _____ , _____ , _____ ,

_____ , _____ , _____ , _____ ,

_____ , _____

5. About what time is it?

_____

6. Add.

$9 + 0 =$ _____

$1 + 7 =$ _____

_____ $= 2 + 5$

_____ $= 4 + 4$

$7 + 7 =$ _____

Displaying Data

1. How many first names are there? _____

2. How many last names are there? _____

3. With which names will you work—first names or last names? _____

4. Make a tally chart for your set of names.

_____ Names	
Number of Letters	**Number of Children**
2	
3	
4	
5	
6	
7	
8	
9	
10 or more	

5. How many letters does the longest name have? _____ letters
    The number of letters in the longest name is called the **maximum.**

6. How many letters does the shortest name have? _____ letters
    The number of letters in the shortest name is called the **minimum.**

7. What is the **range** of the numbers of letters? _____ letters
    (*Hint:* If you don't remember what the range is,
    look it up in your *Student Reference Book.*)

Challenge

8. What is the **mode** of the set of data? _____ letters

Displaying Data (cont.)

9. Make a bar graph for your set of data.

Title: _____

Name-Collection Boxes

1. Write 10 names in the 20-box.

┌─────┐
│ **20** │
└─────┘

2. Write 10 names in the 24-box.

┌─────┐
│ **24** │
└─────┘

3. Three names do not belong in this box. Cross them out. Then write the name of the box on the tag.

fourteen

10 + 6

10 less than 26

10 − 6

8 twos

4 + 4 + 4

half of 32

10 + 2 − 4 + 6 − 8 + 10

4. Make up your own box.

Math Boxes 1.6

1. Complete the pattern.

SRB 172 173

2. 6,347

What value does the 6 have? _____

What value does the 7 have? _____

What value does the 3 have? _____

What value does the 4 have? _____

SRB 18 19

3. Use ℗, Ⓝ, Ⓓ, and Ⓠ.

Show $0.89 in two ways.

4. How many trees have exactly 6 bugs? _____

How many trees have exactly 3 bugs? _____

Number of Bugs per Tree	Number of Trees
2	//
3	/
4	////
5	/
6	//

SRB 70–72

5. Count by 10s.

___23___ , _____ , _____ , ___53___ ,

_____ , _____ , _____ , _____ ,

_____ , _____ , _____ , _____ ,

_____

6. Add.

$4 + 8 =$ _____

_____ $= 9 + 2$

$4 + 3 =$ _____

$5 + 5 =$ _____

_____ $= 8 + 8$

SRB 44 45

Finding Differences

									0
1	2	3	4	5	6	7	8	9	10
11	12	13	14	15	16	17	18	19	20
21	22	23	24	25	26	27	28	29	30
31	32	33	34	35	36	37	38	39	40
41	42	43	44	45	46	47	48	49	50
51	52	53	54	55	56	57	58	59	60
61	62	63	64	65	66	67	68	69	70
71	72	73	74	75	76	77	78	79	80
81	82	83	84	85	86	87	88	89	90
91	92	93	94	95	96	97	98	99	100
101	102	103	104	105	106	107	108	109	110

Use the number grid to help you solve these problems.

1. Which is less, 83 or 43? _____   How much less? _____

2. Which is less, 33 or 78? _____   How much less? _____

3. Which is more, 90 or 55? _____   How much more? _____

4. Which is more, 44 or 52? _____   How much more? _____

Find the **difference** between each pair of numbers.

5. 71 and 92 _____   6. 26 and 46 _____

7. 30 and 62 _____   8. 48 and 84 _____

9. 43 and 60 _____   10. 88 and 110 _____

Use with Lesson 1.7.

Skip Counting on the Number Grid

1. Start at 0 and count by 4s on the number grid.
   Mark an X through each number in your count.

2. Start at 0 again and count by 5s on the number grid.
   Draw a circle around each number in your count.

									0
1	2	3	4	5	6	7	8	9	10
11	12	13	14	15	16	17	18	19	20
21	22	23	24	25	26	27	28	29	30
31	32	33	34	35	36	37	38	39	40
41	42	43	44	45	46	47	48	49	50
51	52	53	54	55	56	57	58	59	60
61	62	63	64	65	66	67	68	69	70
71	72	73	74	75	76	77	78	79	80
81	82	83	84	85	86	87	88	89	90
91	92	93	94	95	96	97	98	99	100
101	102	103	104	105	106	107	108	109	110
111	112	113	114	115	116	117	118	119	120
121	122	123	124	125	126	127	128	129	130
131	132	133	134	135	136	137	138	139	140
141	142	143	144	145	146	147	148	149	150
151	152	153	154	155	156	157	158	159	160
161	162	163	164	165	166	167	168	169	170
171	172	173	174	175	176	177	178	179	180
181	182	183	184	185	186	187	188	189	190
191	192	193	194	195	196	197	198	199	200

3. List the numbers that are marked with both an X and a circle.

___ ___ ___ ___ ___ ___ ___ ___ ___ ___

Math Boxes 1.7

1. Write 5 names in the 25-box.

25

14 15

2. Fill in the missing numbers.

	352		

	373	

SRB
7 8

3. Write the number that is 100 more.

16 _____

104 _____

950 _____

Write the number that is 100 less.

249 _____

527 _____

SRB
18 19

4. Count back by 4s.

_104_ , _____ , _____ , _____ ,

_88_ , _____ , _____ , _____ ,

_____ , _____ , _____ , _____ ,

_____ , _____ , _____ , _____

5. Draw hands on the clock to show 6:45.

6. Add.

2 + 8 = _____

5 + 3 = _____

_____ = 6 + 7

_____ = 7 + 9

5 + 8 = _____

44 45

Using a Calculator

Math Message

Use your calculator.

1. Sharon read the first 115 pages of her book last week. She read the rest of the book this week. If she read 86 pages this week, how many pages long is her book?

   Answer: Her book is _____ pages long.

   Number model: _____

2. The paper clip was invented in 1868. The stapler was invented in 1900. How many years after the paper clip was the stapler invented?

   Answer: The stapler was invented _____ years later.

   Number model: _____

3. $28 + 64 + 39 =$ _____

4. $2,648 - 1,576 =$ _____

Calculator Practice

Use your calculator.

5. Begin at 25. Count up by 6s. Record your counts below.

   25 ___ ___ ___ ___ ___ ___ ___ ___ ___ ___

6. Begin at 90. Count back by 9s.

   90 ___ ___ ___ ___ ___ ___ ___ ___ ___

Solve the calculator puzzles.

7. Enter	Change to	How?	8. Enter	Change to	How?
42	92	_____	362	862	_____
61	11	_____	722	3,722	_____
136	216	_____	1,604	804	_____
78	108	_____	9,364	9,964	_____
108	88	_____			

Use with Lesson 1.8.

Math Boxes 1.8

1. What is today's date?

_____

What will be the date in 11 days?

_____

What will be the date in 2 weeks?

_____

2. 1,942

What value does the 4 have? _____

What value does the 9 have? _____

What value does the 1 have? _____

What value does the 2 have? _____

SRB
18 19

3. Use Ⓠ, Ⓓ, Ⓝ, and Ⓟ.

Show $1.48 in two ways.

4. Find the difference between

74 and 24 _____

48 and 35 _____

60 and 39 _____

26 and 15 _____

SRB
8

5. Complete the bar graph.

Player A scores 4 points.

Player B scores 8 points.

Player C scores 3 points.

Player D scores 9 points.

SRB
80 81

6. Add.

$9 + 5 =$ _____

$3 + 7 =$ _____

$5 + 6 =$ _____

_____ $= 6 + 8$

_____ $= 9 + 3$

SRB
44 45

Using Coins

Math Message

1. You buy a carton of juice for 65 cents. Show two ways to pay for it with exact change. Draw Ⓟs to show pennies, Ⓝs to show nickels, Ⓓs to show dimes, and Ⓠs to show quarters.

   a. _____   b. _____

Write each of the following amounts in dollars-and-cents notation.
The first one is done for you.

Example

three dimes and one nickel $0.35

2. five dimes and seven pennies _____

3. fourteen dimes _____

4. two quarters and four pennies _____

5. three dollars and one nickel and three pennies _____

6. seven dollars and eight dimes _____

Write =, <, or >.

7. three quarters _____ three dimes

8. ten dimes _____ one dollar

9. $0.67 _____ seven dimes

10. $1.18 _____ Ⓠ Ⓠ Ⓠ Ⓠ Ⓠ

11. Ⓓ Ⓓ Ⓝ Ⓝ Ⓝ Ⓟ Ⓟ _____ Ⓠ Ⓝ Ⓟ

12. $2.05 _____ $2.50

> **Remember**
> = means *is equal to*
> < means *is less than*
> > means *is greater than*

13. Circle the digit that represents dimes.

$17.63

14. Circle the digit that represents cents.

$18.38

15. Circle the digit that represents dimes.

35¢

16. Jean wants to buy a carton of milk for 35¢.
How much change will she get from 2 quarters?_____

Use ⓠ, ⓓ, ⓝ, and ⓟ to show her change in two ways.

_____

Challenge

Use the Vending Machine Poster on *Student Reference Book,* page 236.

17. Marcy wants to get a strawberry yogurt drink and a chocolate milk from the vending machine. She has only dollar bills.

    a. If the Exact Change light is on, can she buy what she

         wants? _____

    b. If the Exact Change is off, how many dollar bills will she

         put in the machine? _____

         How much change will she get? _____

Math Boxes 1.9

1. Write 5 names in the 75-box.

75

SRB
14 15

2. Fill in the missing numbers.

	632		
			644

SRB
7 8

3. What is 10 more?

614 _____

994 _____

2,462 _____

What is 100 more?

237 _____

3,965 _____

SRB
18 19

4. Count back.

___1,011___ , ___1,010___ , _____ ,

_____ , _____ , _____ ,

_____ , _____ , _____ ,

_____ , _____ , _____ ,

_____ , _____

5. What time does the clock show?

_____

What time will it
be in 30 minutes? _____

6. Add.

3 + 6 = _____

_____ = 5 + 7

8 + 6 = _____

9 + 9 = _____

6 + 4 = _____

SRB
44 45

A Shopping Trip

Use the Stationery Store Poster on *Student Reference Book,* page 238.

1. List the items you are buying in the space below. You must buy at least 3 items. You can buy 2 of the same item, but list it twice.

Item	Sale Price
_____	_____
_____	_____
_____	_____

2. Estimate how many dollar bills you will need to give the

   shopkeeper to pay for your items. _____ dollar bills

3. Give the shopkeeper the dollar bills.

4. The shopkeeper calculates the total cost using a calculator.

   You owe $_____.

5. The shopkeeper calculates the change you should be getting. $_____

6. Use Ⓟ, Ⓝ, Ⓓ, Ⓠ, and $1 to show the change you got

   from the shopkeeper. _____

Challenge

7. Henry buys one pack of batteries and a box of crayons. How much money does he save buying them on sale instead of paying the regular price?

	Regular Price	Sale Price		Difference
batteries	$_____.____	$_____.____	Regular total	$_____.____
crayons	$_____.____	$_____.____	Sale total	$_____.____
Total Cost	$_____.____	$_____.____	**Amount Saved**	$_____.____

Use with Lesson 1.10.

Coin Collections   19

Get your coin collection or grab a handful of coins from the classroom collection. Complete the problems below.

1. Count each kind of coin. Give a total value for each type of coin.

    _____ Ⓟ = $_____._____

    _____ Ⓝ = $_____._____

    _____ Ⓓ = $_____._____

    _____ Ⓠ = $_____._____

2. What is the total value of all the coins? You may use a calculator.

    Total value = $_____._____

3. In the space below, draw a picture of your total. Use as few $1, Ⓠ, Ⓓ, Ⓝ, and Ⓟ as possible.

Challenge

4. Explain how you would enter your total amount on the calculator.

    _____

    _____

    _____

5. Explain how you would go up to the next dollar amount without clearing your calculator. (*Hint:* A dollar amount is $1.00, $2.00, $3.00, and so on.)

    _____

    _____

    _____

Math Boxes 1.10

1. Use addition or subtraction to complete these problems on your calculator.

Enter	Change to	How?
894	2,894	_____
366	66	_____
27,581	28,581	_____
3,775	3,175	_____

2. In the number 38,642

the 4 means ___40___

the 8 means _____

the 6 means _____

the 3 means _____

3. Draw the bills and coins in two ways. $2.43

4. Find the difference between

87 and 37 _____

72 and 55 _____

90 and 49 _____

47 and 26 _____

5. Write <, >, or =.

69 _____ 96

101 _____ 110

2ⓠ _____ 5Ⓓ

1,000 _____ 999

6. Complete the bar graph.

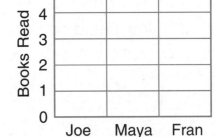

Book Club Totals

Joe read 3 books.

Maya read 2 books.

Fran read 4 books.

Total books read: _____

(unit)

Frames and Arrows

Math Message

Find the pattern. Fill in the missing numbers.

1. 37, 40, 43, _____, _____, _____

2. 27, 25, _____, 21, _____, _____

3. _____, 11, 15, _____, 23, _____

4. _____, _____, 36, 33, _____, 27

Frames and Arrows

5.

6.

7.

8.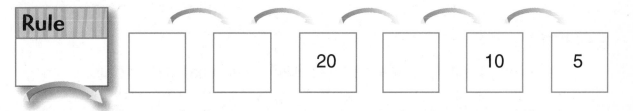

9. Make up one of your own.

Patterns

Complete the number-grid puzzles.

1.

	52	
	62	

2.

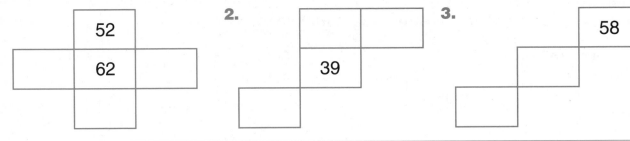

(grid with 39)

3.

(grid with 58)

4. Draw dots to show what comes next.

5. Janie owns a magic calculator. When someone enters a number and then presses the ⊜ key, it changes the number. Here is what happened:

- Tom entered 15. He pressed ⊜ and the calculator showed 5.

- Mary entered 12. She pressed ⊜ and the calculator showed 2.

- Regina entered 27. She pressed ⊜ and the calculator showed 17.

6. What do you think the calculator will show if Janie enters 109 and ⊜? _____

7. Explain how you know. _____

Challenge

8. The numbers below have a pattern. Fill in the missing numbers. Be careful: The same thing does not always happen each time.

   4, 14, 24, 22, 32, 42, 40, 50, 60, 58, _____, _____, _____

9. Describe the pattern. _____

_____

_____

Tic-Tac-Toe Addition

Draw a line through any three numbers whose sum is the target number in the square. The numbers may be in a row, in a column, or on a diagonal. Draw more than one line for each sum.

8		
5	2	1
1	3	7
6	2	0

14		
3	4	7
1	8	6
5	1	3

18		
6	4	9
5	8	5
7	6	4

20		
12	1	9
4	3	6
8	7	5

Think of some other Tic-Tac-Toe puzzles and write them below.

Math Boxes 1.11

---

1. Write 5 names in the 100-box.

100

SRB
14 15

---

2. Fill in the missing numbers.

	713

SRB
7 8

---

3. Write the number that is

     10 less   100 less   1,000 less

4,321 _____

6,942 _____

7,011 _____

8,002 _____

SRB
18 19

---

4. Count back.

_____13_____ , _____ , _____ , _____ ,

_____ , _____ , _____ , _____ ,

_____ , ____4____ , _____ , _____ ,

_____ , _____ , _____ , _____ ,

_____

---

5. About what time is it?

_____

How many minutes
until 2:00? _____

---

6. Add.

4 + 9 = _____

2 + 6 = _____

8 + 7 = _____

_____ = 6 + 6

_____ = 9 + 8

SRB
44 45

Math Boxes 1.12

1. Use addition or subtraction to complete these problems on your calculator.

Enter	Change to	How?
4,501	1,501	_____
173	873	_____
15,604	16,604	_____
9,646	9,346	_____

SRB 18 19

2. Write the number that has

4 hundreds

6 thousands

7 ones

2 tens

_____

Read it to a partner.

 SRB 18 19

3. I spend $3.25 at the store. I give the cashier a $5.00 bill.

How much change should I get?

_____

4. Find the difference between

91 and 21 _____

53 and 15 _____

70 and 29 _____

83 and 57 _____

 SRB 8

5.

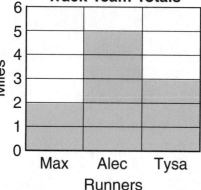

Track Team Totals

Max ran _____ miles.

Alec ran _____ miles.

Tysa ran _____ miles.

SRB 80 81

6. Fill in the empty frames.

Rule

+6

SRB 176 177

Finding Elapsed Times

Write the time shown on the first two clocks below. For the third clock, draw the hands to match the time.

1.

2.

3.

9:15

_____   _____

4. Megan leaves to go swimming at 4:05 and returns at 5:25. How long has she been gone?

_____

5. Robert rides his bike 37 miles. He rides from 10:15 A.M. until 3:50 P.M. How long does it take him to ride 37 miles?

_____

6. Joy leaves for school at the time shown on the first clock. She returns home at the time shown on the second clock. How long is Joy away from home?

_____

Challenge

7. Peter baked cookies for a class party. He baked several different kinds. He began baking at the time shown on the first clock and finished at the time shown on the second clock. How long did it take Peter to bake the cookies?

_____

Math Boxes 1.13

1. Complete the fact family.

$6 + 7 =$ _____

$7 +$ _____ $= 13$

$13 - 6 =$ _____

_____ $- 7 = 6$

2. Lara brought 14 candies to school. She gave away 7 during recess. How many candies does she have now?

_____ candies

3. Allison swam 16 laps in the pool. Melodia swam 9. How many more laps did Allison swim than Melodia?

_____ laps

4. Marque had $6. His mother gave him $8. How much money does Marque have now?

$_____

5. Andre scored 7 points. Tina scored 5 points. How many points did they score altogether?

_____ points

6. Add.

$0 + 7 =$ _____

$5 + 1 =$ _____

$3 + 3 =$ _____

_____ $= 4 + 7$

_____ $= 9 + 6$

1. Write 5 names in the 120-box.

120

14   15

2. In the number 76,135

the 1 means _____ /00 _____

the 7 means _____

the 6 means _____

the 3 means _____

18   19

3. Show $21.62 in two ways.

4. Find the rule. Fill in the empty frames.

 Rule

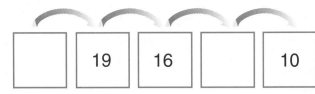

| | 19 | 16 | | 10 |

176 177

5. Write <, >, or =.

42,617 ☐ 42,429

6,589 ☐ 6,859

1,069 ☐ 10,691

Make up your own.

 ☐ _____

13

6. Find the difference between

84 and 14 _____

68 and 25 _____

50 and 16 _____

66 and 42 _____

8

Fact Families and Number Families

Complete the Fact Triangles. Write the fact families.

1.

____ + ____ = ____

____ + ____ = ____

____ − ____ = ____

____ − ____ = ____

2.

____ = ____ + ____

____ = ____ + ____

____ = ____ − ____

____ = ____ − ____

3.

____ + ____ = ____

____ + ____ = ____

____ − ____ = ____

____ − ____ = ____

Complete the number triangles. Write the number families.

4.

____ = ____ + ____

____ = ____ + ____

____ = ____ − ____

____ = ____ − ____

5.

____ + ____ = ____

____ + ____ = ____

____ − ____ = ____

____ − ____ = ____

6.

____ = ____ + ____

____ = ____ + ____

____ = ____ − ____

____ = ____ − ____

Name-Collection Boxes

1. Three names do not belong. Mark them with a big **X**.

100

$$1,680 - 1,580$$

$$25 + 25 + 25$$

$$30 + 70$$

$$\begin{array}{r} 80 \\ + 30 \\ \hline \end{array}$$

$$\begin{array}{r} 1,000 \\ - 100 \\ \hline \end{array}$$

$$\begin{array}{r} 63 \\ + 37 \\ \hline \end{array}$$

$$\begin{array}{r} 9,999 \\ - 9,899 \\ \hline \end{array}$$

2 fifties

$$48 + 52$$

2. Write at least 10 names for 40.

40

3. Write at least 10 names for 200.

200

4. Write at least 10 names for 1,000.

1,000

Use with Lesson 2.2.

Using Basic Facts to Solve Fact Extensions

Fill in the unit box.

Unit

Complete the fact extensions.

1. _____ = 12 − 7

_____ = 120 − 70

_____ = 1,200 − 700

2. 8 + 3 = _____

80 + 30 = _____

800 + 300 = _____

3. _____ = 7 + 6

_____ = 70 + 60

_____ = 700 + 600

Complete the fact extensions.

4. _____ = 6 + 8

_____ = 16 + 8

_____ = 56 + 8

5. 14 − 9 = _____

24 − 9 = _____

54 − 9 = _____

6. _____ = 17 − 11

_____ = 27 − 11

_____ = 47 − 11

Use addition or subtraction to complete these problems on your calculator.

7. Enter	Change to	How?
33	40	_____
80	73	_____
80	23	_____

8. Enter	Change to	How?
430	500	_____
700	640	_____
1,000	400	_____

9. Why is it important to know the basic addition and subtraction facts?

_____

_____

_____

Math Boxes 2.2

---

1. I spent $7.88 at the store. I gave the cashier a $10 bill. How much change should I get back?

$ _____

---

2. Write the +,− fact family for 8, 7, and 15.

_____ + _____ = _____

_____ + _____ = _____

_____ − _____ = _____

_____ − _____ = _____

SRB 48 49

---

3. Use your calculator to find the total.

4 $1 = $ _____ . _____

3 Ⓠ = $ _____ . _____

5 Ⓓ = $ _____ . _____

7 Ⓝ = $ _____ . _____

2 Ⓟ = $ _____ . _____

Total $ _____ . _____

---

4. What time is it?

_____

What time will it be in 20 minutes?

_____

How many minutes until 5:15?

_____

---

5. Put these numbers in order from smallest to largest.

1,060   _____

1,600   _____

1,006   _____

6,001   _____

SRB 13

---

6. Fill in the missing numbers.

	1,073		
		1,104	

SRB 7 8

Use with Lesson 2.2.

Date _____   Time _____

Math Boxes 2.3

1. Write the number that is

	10 less	100 more	1,000 more
368	_____	_____	_____
4,789	_____	_____	_____
40,870	_____	_____	_____
1,999	_____	_____	_____

SRB 18 19

2. Complete the fact extensions.

13 = 6 + 7   **Unit**

_____ = 16 + 7

_____ = 26 + 7

_____ = 106 + 7

_____ = 136 + 7

3. Show $6.62 in two other ways.

$5

Q Q
Q Q
Q Q
N N
P P

4. Fill in the empty frames.

 Rule +100

| | | 935 | | |

SRB 176 177

5. Fill in <, >, or =.

49 ☐ 495

3,000 ☐ 300

69 hundreds ☐ 69 thousands

SRB 13

6. Fill in the missing numbers.

___ ___ 8 ___ ___ 20 ___

SRB 10

Use with Lesson 2.3.   (thirty-three) **33**

"What's My Rule?"

Fill in the blanks.

1.

in	out
100	
120	
70	
150	
200	

2.

in	out
	30
	50
	100
	200
	0

3.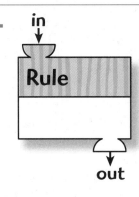

in	out
	13
	23
	43
	73
	93

4.

in	out
14	23
34	43
44	53
64	73
94	103

5.

in	out
35	20
	45
20	
50	35
46	

6.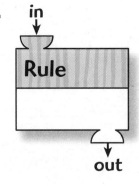

in	out
6	13
9	
5	
4	11
	18

      Use with Lesson 2.3.

Fact Families and Number Families

1. Complete the Fact Triangles. Write the fact families.

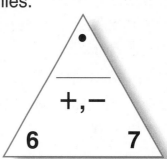

_____ + _____ = _____   _____ + _____ = _____

_____ + _____ = _____   _____ + _____ = _____

_____ − _____ = _____   _____ − _____ = _____

_____ − _____ = _____   _____ − _____ = _____

2. Complete the number triangles. Write the number families.

_____ + _____ = _____   _____ + _____ = _____

_____ + _____ = _____   _____ + _____ = _____

_____ − _____ = _____   _____ − _____ = _____

_____ − _____ = _____   _____ − _____ = _____

Enter the first number into your calculator. Use addition or subtraction
to change it to the second number. Then tell what you did.

Enter	Change to	How?		Enter	Change to	How?
3. 54	60	_____		**4.** 230	300	_____
5. 90	81	_____		**6.** 800	720	_____

Number Stories: Animal Clutches

For each number story, write the numbers you know in the parts-and-total diagram. Write ? for the number you want to find. Solve the problem and write a number model.

1. Two pythons laid clutches of eggs. One clutch had 36 eggs. The other had 23 eggs. That was how many eggs in all?

   Answer the question: _____
   (unit)

   Number model: _____

   Check: Does my answer make sense?

Total	
Part	Part

2. A queen termite laid about 6,000 eggs on Monday and about 7,000 eggs on Tuesday. About how many eggs did she lay in all?

   Answer the question: _____
   (unit)

   Number model: _____

   Check: Does my answer make sense?

Total	
Part	Part

3. Two agama lizards laid clutches of eggs. One clutch had 19 eggs. The other had 22 eggs. In all, how many eggs were laid?

   Answer the question: _____
   (unit)

   Number model: _____

   Check: Does my answer make sense?

Total	
Part	Part

4. Two clutches of Mississippi alligator eggs were found. Each clutch had 47 eggs. What was the total number of eggs found?

   Answer the question: _____
   (unit)

   Number model: _____

   Check: Does my answer make sense?

Total	
Part	Part

Number Stories: Animal Clutches (cont.)

5. Three ostriches laid clutches of eggs. The first clutch had 15 eggs, the second had 9 eggs, and the third had 10 eggs. That was how many eggs in all?

    Answer the question: _____
    (unit)

    Number model: _____

    Check: Does my answer make sense?

Total		
Part	**Part**	**Part**

Challenge

6. An alligator clutch had 60 eggs. Only 12 eggs hatched. How many eggs did not hatch?

    Answer the question: _____
    (unit)

    Number model: _____

    Check: Does my answer make sense?

Total	
Part	**Part**

7. Scientists say a green turtle can lay about 1,800 eggs in a lifetime. But only about 400 eggs hatch. About how many eggs do not hatch?

    Answer the question: _____
    (unit)

    Number model: _____

    Check: Does my answer make sense?

Total	
Part	**Part**

8. On a separate sheet of paper, make up and solve a story using the Animal Clutches poster on pages 242 and 243 in your *Student Reference Book*.

    Answer the question: _____
    (unit)

    Number model: _____

    Check: Does my answer make sense?

Total	
Part	**Part**

"What's My Rule?"

Use with Lesson 2.4.

Fill in the blanks.

1.

Rule
Add
20 minutes

in	out
1:00	
2:05	
4:15	
7:45	
8:51	

2.

Rule
Subtract
10 minutes

in	out
	2:00
	3:15
	6:35
	7:42
	9:55

3.

Rule

in	out
2:00	2:50
3:15	4:05
5:30	6:20
	7:55
8:45	

4.

Rule
Add 25¢

in	out
10¢	
20¢	
25¢	
83¢	
$1.00	

5.

Rule
Subtract 10¢

in	out
	20¢
	45¢
	50¢
	63¢
	$1.00

6.

Rule

in	out
10¢	26¢
25¢	41¢
$1.20	$1.36
80¢	
	99¢

Math Boxes 2.4

---

1. I had a $10 bill. I bought $3.92 worth of candy. How much change should I get?

_____

---

2. Complete the Fact Triangle. Write the fact family.

_____ + _____ = _____

_____ + _____ = _____

_____ − _____ = _____

_____ − _____ = _____

SRB
48 49

---

3. Use a calculator to find the total.

2 $1 = $_____

1 Ⓠ = $_____

3 Ⓓ = $_____

8 Ⓝ = $_____

6 Ⓟ = $_____

Total $_____

---

4. "What's My Rule?"

in	out
14	
24	
39	
	42
	65

Rule
Subtract 7

SRB
179 180

---

5. Use addition or subtraction to complete these problems on your calculator.

Enter	Change to	How?
4,501	1,501	_____
173	873	_____
15,604	16,604	_____
9,646	9,346	_____

SRB
18 19

---

6. Find the difference between

71 and 41 _____

93 and 45 _____

60 and 22 _____

87 and 54 _____

SRB
8

Number Stories: Change-to-More and Change-to-Less

For each number story, write the numbers you know in the change diagram. Write ? for the number you want to find. Then solve the problem. Write the answer and a number model.

Unit
dollars

1. David had $22 in his bank account. For his birthday, his grandmother deposited $25 for him. How much money is in his bank account now?

Start	Change	End

Answer the question: _____

Number model: _____

Check: Does my answer make sense?

2. Jennifer had $19 in her bank account. After babysitting, she is able to deposit $38. How much money is in her bank account now?

Start	Change	End

Answer the question: _____

Number model: _____

Check: Does my answer make sense?

3. Omar had $53 in his piggy bank. He used $16 to take his sister to the movies and buy treats. How much money is left in his piggy bank?

Start	Change	End

Answer the question: _____

Number model: _____

Check: Does my answer make sense?

4. Cleo had $37 in her purse. Then Jillian returned $9 that she had borrowed. How much money does Cleo have now?

Start	Change	End

Answer the question: _____

Number model: _____

Check: Does my answer make sense?

Number Stories (cont.)

5. Tyler had $30 in his wallet. At lunch he spent $17. How much money does Tyler have now?

Answer the question: _____

Number model: _____

Check: Does my answer make sense?

6. Andre had $61 in his bank account. He withdrew $48 to take on vacation. How much is left in his account?

Answer the question: _____

Number model: _____

Check: Does my answer make sense?

Challenge

7. Trung had $15 in his piggy bank. After his birthday, he has $60 in his bank. How much money did Trung get as birthday presents?

Answer the question: _____

Number model: _____

Check: Does my answer make sense?

8. Nikhil had $40 in his wallet when he went to the carnival. When he got home, he had $18. How much did he spend at the carnival?

Answer the question: _____

Number model: _____

Check: Does my answer make sense?

Parts-and-Total Number Stories

For each number story, write the numbers you know in the parts-and-total diagram. Write ? for the number you want to find. Then solve the problem. Write the answer and a number model.

1. There were 80 people at the concert on Saturday night and 50 people at the concert on Sunday night. Altogether, how many people went to the concert?

   Answer the question: _____

   (unit)

   Number model: _____

   Check: Does my answer make sense?

Total	
Part	Part

2. About 800 pieces of mail are lost in the United States every day. About how many pieces of mail are lost in 2 days?

   Answer the question: _____

   (unit)

   Number model: _____

   Check: Does my answer make sense?

Total	
Part	Part

3. The Ramirez family drove 600 miles during the first week of their vacation and 900 miles during the second week. How many miles did they drive in all?

   Answer the question: _____

   (unit)

   Number model: _____

   Check: Does my answer make sense?

Total	
Part	Part

Use with Lesson 2.5.

Math Boxes 2.5

---

1. Write <, >, or =.

     45¢ ☐ $0.45

     4Ⓓ ☐ 3Ⓠ

     $1.85 ☐ $3.00

     5Ⓝ ☐ 2Ⓓ, 1Ⓝ

---

2. Find the missing sums.

Unit

4 + 5 = _____

_____ = 14 + 5

24 + 5 = _____

5 + 44 = _____

---

3. Write this number:

six thousand, four hundred twenty-two

_____

Write the words for 5,931.

_____

_____

---

4. The school chorus has 28 second graders and 34 third graders. How many children are the chorus?

_____ children

Total	
Part	**Part**

---

5. How many children like grapes?

_____

How many children like oranges?

_____

Fruit Choice	Number of Children
apples	////
grapes	~~////~~ /
oranges	///
pears	~~////~~ ~~////~~

---

6. Fill in the empty frames. Use two rules.

    +8   −3

17 ◯ ◯ ◯ ◯

◯ ◯ 27

Temperature Differences

Use the map on page 244 in the *Student Reference Book* to answer Problems 1–4.
Write the numbers you know in the comparison diagram. Write ? for the number
you want to find. Then solve the problem. Write the answer and a number model.

1. What is the difference between the normal high
   and low temperatures for San Francisco?

   Answer the question: _____ °F

   Number model: _____

   Check: Does my answer make sense?

Quantity

Quantity	Difference

2. What is the difference between the normal high
   and low temperatures for Minneapolis?

   Answer the question: _____ °F

   Number model: _____

   Check: Does my answer make sense?

Quantity

Quantity	Difference

3. Which city has the *largest* difference between
   the normal high and low temperatures?

   _____ What is the difference? _____ °F

4. Which city has the *smallest* difference between
   the normal high and low temperatures?

   _____ What is the difference? _____ °F

5. The normal January low in Chicago is 25°F
   less than the normal spring low of 38°F.
   What is the normal January low in Chicago?

   Answer the question: _____ °F

   Number model: _____

   Check: Does my answer make sense?

Quantity

Quantity	Difference

Math Boxes 2.6

1. Write at least 5 names for 1,000.

1,000

SRB 14 15

2. Use 15, 12, and 27. Write the number family.

_____

_____

_____

_____

3. 14 dimes = $_____._____

14 nickels = $_____._____

14 quarters = $_____._____

3 quarters and 6 dimes

= $_____._____

4. "What's My Rule?"

in	out
4	
	12
0	
	21

in ↓

Rule
Add 9

out

SRB 179 180

5. Complete the grid.

		9,975	

SRB 7 8

6. Jonah had $52. He bought a CD for $14. How much money does he have now?

_____

Start	Change	End

SRB 186 187

The Partial-Sums Addition Method

Make a ballpark estimate first. Write a number model to show your estimate. Next, solve using the partial-sums method and show your work. Then compare your answers with a partner's. If you disagree, use a calculator. If you did a problem incorrectly, work it again.

Unit
miles

Example

	100s	10s	1s
	3	2	9
+	4	1	8

$$
\begin{array}{r}
7\ 0\ 0 \\
3\ 0 \\
+\ 1\ 7 \\
\hline
7\ 4\ 7
\end{array}
$$

Ballpark estimate:

$300 + 400 = 700$

1.

$$
\begin{array}{r}
43 \\
+\ 26 \\
\end{array}
$$

Ballpark estimate:

_____

2.

$$
\begin{array}{r}
90 \\
+\ 37 \\
\end{array}
$$

Ballpark estimate:

_____

3.

$$
\begin{array}{r}
172 \\
+\ 109 \\
\end{array}
$$

Ballpark estimate:

_____

4.

$$
\begin{array}{r}
87 \\
+\ 113 \\
\end{array}
$$

Ballpark estimate:

_____

5.

$$
\begin{array}{r}
376 \\
+\ 401 \\
\end{array}
$$

Ballpark estimate:

_____

The Partial-Sums Addition Method (cont.)

6.
```
   751
+  757
```

Ballpark estimate:

_____

7.
```
   743
+  504
```

Ballpark estimate:

_____

8.
```
   257
+  245
```

Ballpark estimate:

_____

9.
```
   298
+  419
```

Ballpark estimate:

_____

10.
```
   487
+  313
```

Ballpark estimate:

_____

11.
```
  1,438
+   694
```

Ballpark estimate:

_____

Change-to-More and Change-to-Less Number Stories

Write the numbers you know in the change diagram. Write ? for the number you want to find. Then solve the problem. Write the answer and a number model.

1. Nikki had a collection of 35 beanbag animals. She gave 17 of the animals to her sister. How many does she have now?

Start	Change	End

Answer the question: _____
(unit)

Number model: _____

Check: Does my answer make sense?

2. Lewis delivered newspapers to 27 houses. Fourteen more houses were added to his route. How many houses does he deliver to now?

Start	Change	End

Answer the question: _____
(unit)

Number model: _____

Check: Does my answer make sense?

3. At 5:00 P.M. there were 100 people waiting for the fireworks. By 8:00 P.M. 300 more people had arrived. How many people were waiting then?

Start	Change	End

Answer the question: _____
(unit)

Number model: _____

Check: Does my answer make sense?

4. Make up your own change number story.

_____

_____

Answer the question: _____
(unit)

Start	Change	End

Number model: _____

Check: Does my answer make sense?

Math Boxes 2.7

---

1.   10 more   100 more   1,000 more

65   _____   _____   _____

410   _____   _____   _____

602   _____   _____   _____

1,543   _____   _____   _____

7,095   _____   _____   _____

SRB 18 19

---

2. Fill in the blanks.

$34 + \underline{\hspace{1cm}} = 60$

$\underline{\hspace{1cm}} = 19 + 21$

$100 = 50 + \underline{\hspace{1cm}}$

$70 = \underline{\hspace{1cm}} - 20$

---

3. I spent $4.13 at the store. I gave the cashier $5.00. How much change should I receive?

_____

Draw the fewest number of coins possible to show the change I received.

---

4. Lily had 33 rings in one box and 29 in another. How many did she have in all?   _____ rings

Total	
Part	**Part**

SRB 188 189

---

5. Fill in the empty frames. Use two rules.

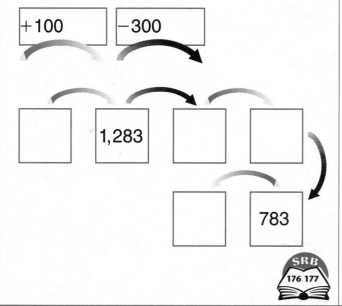

+100   −300

1,283

783

SRB 176 177

---

6. Austin read his book for 45 minutes on Monday and for 25 minutes on Tuesday. How many more minutes did he read on Monday?

_____ minutes

Quantity

Quantity	Difference

SRB 190

The Trade-First Subtraction Method

Solve using the trade-first subtraction method. Show your work.
Use a ballpark estimate to check whether your answer makes
sense. Write a number model for your estimate. Then compare
your answers with a partner's. Use a calculator if you disagree.
If you did a problem incorrectly, work it again.

Unit
miles

Example	**1.**	**2.**
	$$\begin{array}{r} 91 \\ -\ 46 \end{array}$$	$$\begin{array}{r} 63 \\ -\ 38 \end{array}$$

Example

100s	10s	1s
1	14	
2	4	7
−1	8	6

$$\begin{array}{r} 6 \quad 1 \end{array}$$

Ballpark estimate:

$250 - 200 = 50$

Ballpark estimate:

_____

Ballpark estimate:

_____

3.	**4.**	**5.**
$$\begin{array}{r} 129 \\ -\ 112 \end{array}$$	$$\begin{array}{r} 208 \\ -\ 106 \end{array}$$	$$\begin{array}{r} 213 \\ -\ 206 \end{array}$$

Ballpark estimate:

_____

Ballpark estimate:

_____

Ballpark estimate:

_____

The Trade-First Subtraction Method (cont.)   51

6.
$$
\begin{array}{r}
245 \\
-\ 207 \\
\hline
\end{array}
$$

Ballpark estimate:

_____

7.
$$
\begin{array}{r}
283 \\
-\ 256 \\
\hline
\end{array}
$$

Ballpark estimate:

_____

8.
$$
\begin{array}{r}
853 \\
-\ 606 \\
\hline
\end{array}
$$

Ballpark estimate:

_____

9.
$$
\begin{array}{r}
826 \\
-\ 172 \\
\hline
\end{array}
$$

Ballpark estimate:

_____

10.
$$
\begin{array}{r}
752 \\
-\ 387 \\
\hline
\end{array}
$$

Ballpark estimate:

_____

11.
$$
\begin{array}{r}
640 \\
-\ 479 \\
\hline
\end{array}
$$

Ballpark estimate:

_____

Addition Strategies

Use any method you like to solve each addition problem. Show your work. Use a ballpark estimate to check whether your answer makes sense. Write a number model for your estimate.

Example

	100s	10s	1s
	2	3	8
+	4	4	1

$$6\ 0\ 0$$
$$7\ 0$$
$$+\ \ \ \ 9$$
$$\overline{6\ 7\ 9}$$

Ballpark estimate:

$$240 + 440 = 680$$

1.
$$439$$
$$+\ 356$$

Ballpark estimate:

_____

2.
$$318$$
$$+\ 226$$

Ballpark estimate:

_____

3.
$$487$$
$$+\ 258$$

Ballpark estimate:

_____

4.
$$353$$
$$+\ 187$$

Ballpark estimate:

_____

5.
$$754$$
$$+\ 668$$

Ballpark estimate:

_____

Math Boxes 2.8

---

1. Put these numbers in order from smallest to largest.

32,764   _____

8,596   _____

32,199   _____

85,096   _____

SRB
13

---

2. Use 87, 5, and 92. Write 2 addition and 2 subtraction number models.

_____

_____

_____

_____

---

3. Add. Show your work.

$$\begin{array}{r} 27 \\ + \ 48 \\ \hline \end{array} \qquad \begin{array}{r} 152 \\ + \ 394 \\ \hline \end{array}$$

SRB
51 52

---

4. "What's My Rule?"

in	out
10	
21	
32	
	60

in ↓

Rule

Add 4

out

SRB
179 180

---

5. Use your calculator. Write the answers in dollars and cents.

64¢ + $1.73 = $_____._____

$0.85 + 53¢ = $_____._____

$2.08 + $5.01 = $_____._____

37¢ + 26¢ = $_____._____

---

6. Theo had 17 shells in his collection. He found 9 more at the beach. How many shells are in his collection now?

_____ shells

Start	Change	End

SRB
186 187

Number Stories with Three or More Addends

1. José bought milk at 35 cents, apple juice at 55 cents, grape juice at 45 cents, and orange juice at 65 cents. How much money did he spend?

   Answer the question: _____
   (unit)

   Number model:

   _____

   Check: Does my answer make sense?

Total			
Part	Part	Part	Part

2. Michelle drove from Houston, Texas, to Wichita, Kansas. On the first day she drove 245 miles. On the second day she drove 207 miles. On the third day she drove 158 miles and arrived in Wichita. How many miles did she travel in all?

   Answer the question: _____
   (unit)

   Number model:

   _____

   Check: Does my answer make sense?

Total		
Part	Part	Part

3. Zookeepers watched a clutch of 54 python eggs. On the first day, 18 eggs hatched. On the next day, 11 more hatched. How many eggs still had not hatched?

   Answer the question: _____
   (unit)

   Number model:

   _____

   Check: Does my answer make sense?

Total		
Part	Part	Part

Use with Lesson 2.9.

Number Stories with Three or More Addends (cont.)

4. Carl has $2.50 for juice or milk at lunch. On each of 2 days, he buys grape juice for 45 cents. On the third day, he buys milk for 40 cents. How much money does he have left?

Total			
Part	**Part**	**Part**	**Part**

Answer the question: _____
(unit)

Number model:

_____

Check: Does my answer make sense?

---

5. Janna started to read a 128-page book. She read 13 pages before dinner and 39 pages after dinner. How many pages does she have left?

Total		
Part	**Part**	**Part**

Answer the question: _____
(unit)

Number model:

_____

Check: Does my answer make sense?

---

6. The Flores family is driving from Minneapolis, Minnesota, to Bismarck, North Dakota. The distance is 501 miles. They drove 235 miles before lunch. After lunch they drove 150 miles and stopped for a rest. How many more miles will they drive?

Total		
Part	**Part**	**Part**

Answer the question: _____
(unit)

Number model:

_____

Check: Does my answer make sense?

Subtraction Strategies

Solve each subtraction problem using your own method. Show your
work. Use a ballpark estimate to check whether your answer makes
sense. Write a number model for your estimate.

Example	**1.**	**2.**
	$$\begin{array}{r} 93 \\ -\ 47 \\ \hline \end{array}$$	$$\begin{array}{r} 487 \\ -\ 129 \\ \hline \end{array}$$

Example work:

100s	10s	1s
1	12	
2̸	2̸	6
−1	3	4
	9	2

Ballpark estimate:

$$230 - 130 = 100$$

Ballpark estimate:

_____

Ballpark estimate:

_____

3.	**4.**	**5.**
$$\begin{array}{r} 361 \\ -\ 248 \\ \hline \end{array}$$	$$\begin{array}{r} 724 \\ -\ 396 \\ \hline \end{array}$$	$$\begin{array}{r} 515 \\ -\ 367 \\ \hline \end{array}$$

Ballpark estimate:

_____

Ballpark estimate:

_____

Ballpark estimate:

_____

Math Boxes 2.9

1. Fill in the tag. Write at least 5 names for that number.

2. Complete the problems.

Unit

$$\begin{array}{r} 4\ 3\ 0 \\ + \\ \hline 6\ 0\ 0 \end{array} \qquad \begin{array}{r} 9\ 5\ 0 \\ + \\ \hline 1,0\ 0\ 0 \end{array}$$

$$\begin{array}{r} 1,0\ 0\ 0 \\ -\ \ 3\ 0\ 0 \\ \hline \end{array} \qquad \begin{array}{r} 5\ 6\ 0 \\ - \\ \hline 4\ 0\ 0 \end{array}$$

SRB 14 15

3. Subtract. Show your work.

$$\begin{array}{r} 72 \\ -\ 35 \\ \hline \end{array} \qquad \begin{array}{r} 153 \\ -\ 28 \\ \hline \end{array}$$

SRB 54 55

4. There are 17 boys and 24 girls in the math club. How many children in all are in the math club?

_____ children

Total	
Part	**Part**

SRB 188 189

5. About what time is it?

_____

6. Jack answered 29 questions. José answered 37 questions. How many fewer questions did Jack answer than José?

_____ questions

Quantity	

Quantity	Difference

SRB 190

Math Boxes 2.10

1. Which tool would you use to measure the following?

yardstick	ruler	thermometer

temperature _____

height of the ceiling _____

length of your thumb _____

152

2. Circle the best unit of measurement.

distance to Spain

miles   centimeters   inches

width of a crayon

miles   centimeters   feet

length of your journal

miles   yards   inches

123 130

3. Measure the line segment in inches.

_____ inches

125–127

4. Measure the line segment in centimeters.

_____ centimeters

125–127

5. How many squares are shaded?

_____ squares

136–138

6. How long is the fence around the flowers?

_____ feet

3 feet

2 feet   2 feet

3 feet

132 133

Estimating and Measuring Lengths

Work with a partner. Estimate the lengths of things in the classroom in "class shoe" units. Write the estimate. Then use the "class shoe" strip to measure the object. Write the measurement.

Object	Estimate	Measurement
	about _____ "class shoes"	about _____ "class shoes"
	about _____ "class shoes"	about _____ "class shoes"
	about _____ "class shoes"	about _____ "class shoes"
	about _____ "class shoes"	about _____ "class shoes"
	about _____ "class shoes"	about _____ "class shoes"
	about _____ "class shoes"	about _____ "class shoes"
	about _____ "class shoes"	about _____ "class shoes"
	about _____ "class shoes"	about _____ "class shoes"

Why is it important to use the same units everyone else is using to measure things?

_____

_____

_____

_____

Addition and Subtraction Practice

Add or subtract. Make a ballpark estimate to check your answer.
Write a number model for your estimate.

1.
$$\begin{array}{r} 681 \\ + 253 \\ \hline \end{array}$$

Ballpark estimate:

_____

2.
$$\begin{array}{r} 749 \\ + 161 \\ \hline \end{array}$$

Ballpark estimate:

_____

3.
$$\begin{array}{r} 417 \\ + 386 \\ \hline \end{array}$$

Ballpark estimate:

_____

4.
$$\begin{array}{r} 472 \\ - 253 \\ \hline \end{array}$$

Ballpark estimate:

_____

5.
$$\begin{array}{r} 728 \\ - 173 \\ \hline \end{array}$$

Ballpark estimate:

_____

6.
$$\begin{array}{r} 550 \\ - 364 \\ \hline \end{array}$$

Ballpark estimate:

_____

Use with Lesson 3.1.

Math Boxes 3.1

---

1. Show $10.78 in two other ways.

$5
$5
Q Q
D D
N P
P P

---

2. Find the rule and complete the table.

in	out
117	112
119	
	116
	131
142	

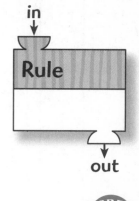

SRB
179 180

---

3. Shade to show the following data.

A is 4 cm.
B is 3 cm.
C is 8 cm.
D is 7 cm.

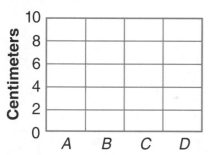

SRB
80 81

---

4. Write a number story by filling in the blanks.

Tom collects coins. He has

_____ quarters, _____ dimes,

_____ nickels, and _____ pennies.

How many coins in all?

_____

SRB
188 189

---

5. Write <, >, or =.

4 + 5 + 6 _____ 3 + 5 + 7

7 + 5 + 9 _____ 6 + 6 + 8

2 + 11 + 4 _____ 7 + 1 + 9

15 + 7 + 5 _____ 9 + 9 + 9

4 + 5 + 6 _____ 3 + 7 + 6

SRB
13

---

6. Add. Show your work.

```
  492          555
+  18        + 192
```

SRB
51 52

Measuring Line Segments

1. Use Ruler A to measure to the nearest inch (in.).

Use Ruler E to measure to the nearest centimeter (cm).

Ruler A   **Ruler E**

about _____ in.   about _____ cm

about _____ in.   about _____ cm

about _____ in.   about _____ cm

2. Use Ruler B to measure to the nearest $\frac{1}{2}$ inch.

Use Ruler E to measure to the nearest $\frac{1}{2}$ centimeter (cm).

Ruler B   **Ruler E**

about _____ in.   about _____ cm

about _____ in.   about _____ cm

about _____ in.   about _____ cm

3. Use Ruler C to measure to the nearest $\frac{1}{4}$ inch.

Use Ruler E to measure to the nearest millimeter (mm).

Ruler C   **Ruler E**

about _____ in.   about _____ mm

about _____ in.   about _____ mm

about _____ in.   about _____ mm

Use with Lesson 3.2.

Math Boxes 3.2

---

1. Complete the puzzle.

9,632

9,665

SRB
7 8

---

2. 53 people were standing in line at 9:00 A.M. 97 people were standing in line at 10:00 A.M. How many more people were standing in line at 10:00 A.M.?

_____ people

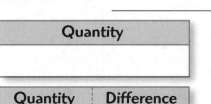

Quantity

Quantity	Difference

SRB
190

---

3. Count by 100s.

___97___ ; _____ ; _____ ;

_____ ; ___497___ ; _____ ;

_____ ; _____ ; _____ ;

_____ ; _____ ; _____

---

4. Subtract. Show your work.

$$943 - 409 \qquad 884 - 299 \qquad 695 - 47$$

SRB
54 55

---

5. It is 7:45 A.M. Draw the hour and minute hands to show the time 15 minutes earlier. What time does the clock show now?

   _____

---

6. Solve.

_____ = 8 + 9

_____ = 48 + 9

9 + 5 = _____

900 + 500 = _____

_____ = 12 − 4

_____ = 12,000 − 4,000

Body Measures

Work with a partner to find each measurement to the nearest $\frac{1}{4}$ inch.

	Adult at Home	Me (Now)	Me (Later)
Date	_____ , _____	_____ , _____	_____ , _____
height	about _____ in.	about _____ in.	about _____ in.
shoe length	about _____ in.	about _____ in.	about _____ in.
around neck	about _____ in.	about _____ in.	about _____ in.
around wrist	about _____ in.	about _____ in.	about _____ in.
waist to floor	about _____ in.	about _____ in.	about _____ in.
forearm	about _____ in.	about _____ in.	about _____ in.
hand span	about _____ in.	about _____ in.	about _____ in.
arm span	about _____ in.	about _____ in.	about _____ in.
_____	about _____ in.	about _____ in.	about _____ in.
_____	about _____ in.	about _____ in.	about _____ in.
_____	about _____ in.	about _____ in.	about _____ in.

←—forearm—→

hand span

←— arm span —→

Use with Lesson 3.3.

Estimating Lengths

1. Follow these steps using **U.S. customary** units: inches (in.), feet (ft), or yards (yd). Then follow these steps using **metric** units: millimeters (mm), centimeters (cm), decimeters (dm), or meters (m).

   • Use personal references to estimate the measures.

   • Record your estimates. Be sure to write the units.

   • Measure with a ruler or tape measure. Record your measurements.

Objects	U.S. Customary Units		Metric Units	
	Estimate	Measurement	Estimate	Measurement
height of your desk				
long side of your calculator				
short side of the classroom				
distance around your head				

2. Choose your own things to estimate and measure.

Objects	U.S. Customary Units		Metric Units	
	Estimate	Measurement	Estimate	Measurement

Math Boxes 3.3

1. Write the number that is

	10 less	100 less	1,000 less
1,067	_____	_____	_____
1,593	_____	_____	_____
2,154	_____	_____	_____
6,163	_____	_____	_____

SRB 18 19

2. Measure to the nearest $\frac{1}{4}$ inch.

_____

_____

Draw a line segment $1\frac{1}{2}$ inches long.

SRB 125–127

3. Choose a 3-digit number and write at least five names for that number.

SRB 14 15

4. Fill in the missing amounts.

I had 38¢. I spent _____.
I have 15¢ left.

I had 54¢. I found _____.
Now I have 83¢.

SRB 190

5. 8 + 6 = _____

8 + 6 + 7 = _____

8 + 6 + 7 + 5 = _____

```
  17        17        17
+  8         8         8
          + 5          5
                    + 19
```

Unit

6. Add. Show your work.

```
  384          8,916
+ 675        + 7,504
```

SRB 51 52

Perimeters of Polygons

1. Record the **perimeter** (the distance around) of your straw rectangle and parallelogram.

   rectangle: about _____ inches   parallelogram: about _____ inches

2. Use a tape measure to find each side and the perimeter.

Polygon	Each Side	Perimeter
triangle	about _____ in., about _____ in., about _____ in.	about _____ in.
triangle	about _____ in., about _____ in., about _____ in.	about _____ in.
square	about _____ in.	about _____ in.
rhombus	about _____ in.	about _____ in.
trapezoid	about _____ in., about _____ in. about _____ in., about _____ in.	about _____ in.

3. Find the perimeter, in inches, of the figures below.

   _____   _____

4. Draw each shape on the centimeter grid.
   square with perimeter = 16 cm   rectangle with perimeter = 20 cm

Measures Hunt

Find out about how long some objects are.

These objects will be **personal references.**

Use your personal references to estimate the lengths of other things.

1. Find things that are about 1 inch long, 1 foot long, and 1 yard long.

   Use a ruler, tape measure, or yardstick.

   List your objects below.

About 1 inch (in.)	About 1 foot (ft)	About 1 yard (yd)
_____	_____	_____
_____	_____	_____
_____	_____	_____
_____	_____	_____
_____	_____	_____

2. Find things that are about 1 centimeter long, 1 decimeter long, and 1 meter long.

   Use a ruler, tape measure, or meterstick.

   List your objects below.

About 1 centimeter (cm)	About 1 decimeter (dm)	About 1 meter (m)
_____	_____	_____
_____	_____	_____
_____	_____	_____
_____	_____	_____

Math Boxes 3.4

---

1. "What's My Rule?"

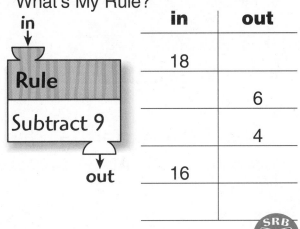

in
↓
Rule

Subtract 9

↓
out

in	out
18	
	6
	4
16	

179 180

---

2. The driving distance between St. Louis and Denver is about 863 miles. If you go by way of Wichita, the distance is about 982 miles. How much farther is it to go by way of Wichita?

_____ miles farther

190

---

3. Fill in the empty frames and the rule box.

+5

6   8

5

176 177

---

4. Subtract. Show your work.

Unit
buttons

$$704 - 86$$

$$6{,}243 - 2{,}948$$

54 55

---

5. Write <, >, or =.

$1\frac{1}{2}$ feet _____ 16 inches

3 feet _____ 2 yards

5 feet _____ 60 inches

55 inches _____ 1 yard

13
128 129

---

6. Measure to the nearest centimeter.

_____

_____

Draw a line segment 7 centimeters long.

119–121

Math Boxes 3.5

1. Find the perimeter.

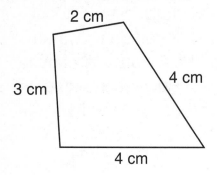

2 cm
4 cm
3 cm
4 cm

perimeter = _____
(unit)

SRB
132 133

2. Measure to the nearest $\frac{1}{4}$ inch.

_____

_____

Draw a line segment $2\frac{1}{2}$ inches long.

SRB
125–127

3. Yuri saved $24.85. He earned $9.95 more. How much did he have then?

_____

SRB
188 189

4. Write the equivalent lengths.

3 yards = _____ ft

_____ inches = 2 yards

50 millimeters = _____ centimeters

3 meters = _____ centimeters

SRB
122
128 129

5. Add.

9 + 22 + 11 = _____

13 + 17 + 16 = _____

24 + 6 + 9 = _____

6. Make a ballpark estimate to check that the answer makes sense.

492 + 108 = _____

about _____

_____ = 648 + 209

about _____

SRB
167

Geoboard Perimeters

Materials ☐ geoboard and rubber bands, or geoboard dot paper

Work with a partner.

1. Suppose that the distance between two pins is 1 unit. Make a rectangle with a perimeter of 14 units. Use rubber bands and a geoboard, or draw the rectangle on dot paper. Record the lengths of the sides in the table.

2. Now make a different rectangle that also has a perimeter of 14 units. Record the lengths of the sides for this shape.

3. Complete the table for other perimeters.

4. Try to make a rectangle or square with a perimeter of 13 units.

5. Try to make other rectangles or squares with perimeters that are an odd number of units.

Geoboard Perimeters		
Perimeter	Longer sides	Shorter sides
14 units	_____ units	_____ units
14 units	_____ units	_____ units
14 units	_____ units	_____ units
12 units	_____ units	_____ units
12 units	_____ units	_____ units
12 units	_____ units	_____ units
16 units	_____ units	_____ units
16 units	_____ units	_____ units
16 units	_____ units	_____ units
16 units	_____ units	_____ units

Challenge

Change the unit. Now 1 unit is double the distance between two points. Make a rectangle or square whose perimeter is an odd number of units.

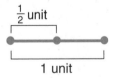

Follow-Up

Look for a pattern in your table. Can you find one? Now, do not use a geoboard or dot paper. Find the lengths of the sides of a rectangle or square with a perimeter of 24 units. Then make or draw the shape to check your answer.

Tiling with Pattern Blocks

Materials ❏ pattern blocks: square, triangle, narrow rhombus

❏ crayons

Work with a partner.

1. Use square pattern blocks. Look at the top rectangle on the next page. Cover as much of the rectangle as you can, placing all of the blocks inside it. There may be uncovered spaces at the edges. Do not overlap the blocks. Line them up so that there are no gaps. This is called **"tiling."**

2. Count and record the number of blocks you used.

3. Trace around the edges of each block. Then color any spaces not covered by blocks. Estimate how many blocks would be needed to cover the colored spaces.

4. Record how many blocks are needed to cover the whole rectangle.

5. Tile the second rectangle with triangles. Repeat Steps 2–4 above.

6. Tile the third rectangle with narrow rhombuses. Repeat Steps 2–4 above.

Follow-Up

7. The **area** of a shape is a measure of the space inside the shape. You measured the area of a rectangle three ways: with squares, triangles, and narrow rhombuses. Record the areas below.

   The area of the rectangle is about _____ squares.

   The area of the rectangle is about _____ triangles.

   The area of the rectangle is about _____ narrow rhombuses.

8. Which of the three pattern blocks has the largest area? _____

   Which has the smallest area? _____

   How did you decide? _____

   _____

Cover this rectangle with squares.

About _____ squares cover the whole rectangle.

Cover this rectangle with triangles.

About _____ triangles cover the whole rectangle.

Cover this rectangle with narrow rhombuses.

About _____ narrow rhombuses cover the whole rectangle.

Straw Triangles

Materials   ❏ 4-inch, 6-inch, and 8-inch straws

❏ twist-ties

Work in a group to make as many different-size triangles as you can out of the straws and twist-ties. (Be sure that straws are touching at all ends.) Before you start, decide how you will share the work.

For each triangle, record the length of each side and the perimeter in the chart. The triangle made out of the shortest straws is already recorded.

Straw Triangles			
Side 1	**Side 2**	**Side 3**	**Perimeter**
4 in.	4 in.	4 in.	12 in.

Follow-Up

Discuss these questions with others in your group.

1. Which triangles have similar shapes?

_____

2. Which pairs of triangles have the same perimeter?

_____

3. By looking at your constructions, estimate which triangle of each pair of triangles in problem 2 has the larger area (space inside the triangles).

_____

4. What happens if you try to make a triangle out of two 4-inch straws and one 8-inch straw?

_____

Areas of Rectangles

Draw each rectangle on the grid. Make a dot inside each small square in your rectangle.

1. Draw a 3-by-5 rectangle.

Area = _____ square units

2. Draw a 6-by-8 rectangle.

Area = _____ square units

3. Draw a 9-by-5 rectangle.

Area = _____ square units

Fill in the blanks.

4.

This is a _____-by-_____ rectangle.

Area = _____ square units

5.

This is a _____-by-_____ rectangle.

Area = _____ square units

6.

This is a _____-by-_____ rectangle.

Area = _____ square units

7.

This is a _____-by-_____ rectangle.

Area = _____ square units

Math Boxes 3.6

1. Put these numbers in order from smallest to largest:

47,912 _____ ← smallest

47,192 _____

49,271 _____

49,172 _____ ← largest

2. Solve.

Unit

_____ = 7 + 9

_____ = 37 + 9

16 − 8 = _____

76 − 8 = _____

6 + 5 = _____

600 + 500 = _____

3. There were 144 cartons of milk delivered to school. 84 of the cartons were chocolate milk. The rest were 2% milk. How many cartons of 2% milk were delivered?

_____ cartons

4. Subtract. Show your work.

$$\begin{array}{r} 384 \\ -\ 175 \end{array} \qquad \begin{array}{r} 8{,}306 \\ -\ 7{,}574 \end{array}$$

5. When I left home, I had $4.00. I spent 73¢ at the fruit stand and $2.59 at the grocery store. How much did I spend in all?

_____

How much do I have when I go home?

_____

6. Measure to the nearest centimeter.

_____

_____

Draw a line segment 4 centimeters long.

Use with Lesson 3.6.

More Areas of Rectangles

Make a dot inside each small square in one row. Then fill in the blanks.

1.

Squares in a row: _____

Number of rows: _____

Number model:

_____ × _____ = _____

Area = _____ square units

2.

Squares in a row: _____

Number of rows: _____

Number model:

_____ × _____ = _____

Area = _____ square units

3.

Squares in a row: _____

Number of rows: _____

Number model:

_____ × _____ = _____

Area = _____ square units

Now, draw the rectangle on the grid. Then fill in the blanks.

4. Draw a 5-by-7 rectangle.

Number model:

_____ × _____ = _____

Area = _____ square units

5. Draw an 8-by-8 rectangle.

Number model:

_____ × _____ = _____

Area = _____ square units

6. Draw a 3-by-9 rectangle.

Number model:

_____ × _____ = _____

Area = _____ square units

Math Boxes 3.7

1. What is the perimeter?

3 cm

4 cm

2 cm

2 cm

4 cm

3.5 cm

_____
(unit)

SRB
132 133

2. Measure to the nearest $\frac{1}{4}$ inch.

_____

_____

Draw a line segment $2\frac{3}{4}$ inches long.

SRB
125 126

3. At 7:00 A.M., the temperature was 23°F. At 10:00 A.M., the temperature was 40°F. How much warmer was it at 10:00 A.M. than at 7:00 A.M.?

_____°F warmer

SRB
186 187

4. Write <, >, or =.

6 decimeters ⬜ 60 millimeters

3 yards ⬜ 36 inches

2 centimeters ⬜ 4 meters

Write your own.

_____ ⬜ _____

SRB
122
128 129

5. Complete the number story.

Amber ate _____ grapes.

Zack ate _____ grapes.

Sophie ate _____ grapes.

_____ grapes were eaten in all.

SRB
188 189

6. Add. Show your work.

```
   38          182
  698          309
+ 202          962
             + 745
```

SRB
51–53

Diameters and Circumferences

1. Find numbers on the label of your can. Write some of them below. Also write the unit if there is one.

   _____   _____

2. Record the diameter and circumference of your can.

   can letter _____ **diameter:** about _____ cm **circumference:** about _____ cm

3. Write the rule linking diameter and circumference:

   _____

Review

4.

in	out
5	
50	
500	
5,000	

5.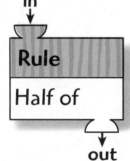

in	out
12	
120	
1,200	
12,000	

6.

in	out
3	6
	20
5	10
70	
	400

7.

Math Boxes 3.8

1.

Area: _____ square cm

2. Subtract.

49 − 17 = _____

69 − 17 = _____

199 − 17 = _____

2,119 − 17 = _____

9,139 − 17 = _____

3. Find the total value.

4 $1

3 Q

6 D

2 N

7 P

Total $_____

4. Subtract. Show your work.

Unit

```
  563        807
− 294      − 429
```

5.

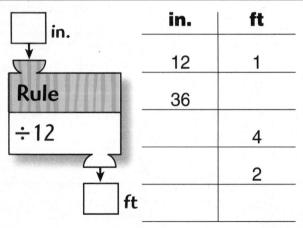

in.	ft
12	1
36	
	4
	2

6. Measure to the nearest millimeter.

_____

_____

Draw a line segment 20 millimeters long.

Units of Linear Measure

Choose a U.S. customary unit and a metric unit for each object.
Put a check in the box.

	U.S. Customary				Metric			
	in.	ft	yd	mi	mm	cm	m	km
thickness of a magazine								
length of hair								
diameter of a quarter								
height of a building								
distance to Paris								
length of a baseball bat								
circumference of a telephone pole								
perimeter of a baseball diamond								
depth of a lake								
Make up your own.								

Math Boxes 3.9

---

1. How many rows? _____

How many columns? _____

How many dots in all? _____

2. There are 3 cars. 4 people are riding in each car. How many people in all?

_____ people

---

3. 2 children share 12 toys equally. How many toys does each child get?

_____ toys

4. Each child has 4 lollipops. There are 16 lollipops. How many children are there?

_____ children

---

5. Three children share 10 sticks of gum equally. How many sticks does each child get?

_____ stick(s)

How many sticks are left over?

_____ stick(s)

6. $5 \times 0 =$ _____

$1 \times 8 =$ _____

$2 \times 3 =$ _____

_____ $= 5 \times 3$

_____ $= 4 \times 10$

Solving Multiplication Number Stories

Use the Variety Store Poster on page 239 of the *Student Reference Book.*

For each number story:

- Fill in a multiplication/division diagram with the numbers you know.
  Write ? for the number you need to find.
- Use counters, draw pictures, or do whatever helps you find the answer.
- Record the answer with its unit. Check whether your answer makes sense.

1. Yosh has 4 boxes of mini stock cars.
   How many cars does he have?

   Answer: _____
   (unit)

boxes	cars per box	total number of cars

2. How many cards are in 5 packages of file cards?

   Answer: _____
   (unit)

packages	cards per package	total number of cards

3. Claire buys 8 packages of fashion pens. How many pens does she have?

   Answer: _____
   (unit)

packages	pens per package	total number of pens

4. If your mother buys 2 packages of bright shoelaces, how many pairs of shoelaces does she buy?

   Answer: _____
   (unit)

packages	pairs of shoelaces per package	total number of pairs of shoelaces

Bonus: About how much do the 2 packages cost? _____

Writing Multiplication Number Stories

Write 2 multiplication stories. For each story:

• Fill in the multiplication/division diagram. Write ? for the number you need to find.

• Use counters, draw pictures, or do whatever helps you find the answer.

• Record your answer with its unit. Check whether your answer makes sense.

1. _____

_____

_____

Answer: _____
                        (unit)

2. _____

_____

_____

Answer: _____
                        (unit)

Use with Lesson 4.1.

Measuring Line Segments

Use your ruler to measure each line segment.

Measure to the nearest $\frac{1}{2}$ inch.

1. _____

   about _____ inches

2. _____

   about _____ inches

3. _____

   about _____ inches

Measure to the nearest $\frac{1}{4}$ inch.

4. _____

   about _____ inches

5. _____

   about _____ inches

Measure as precisely as you can.

6. _____

   about _____ inches

Math Boxes 4.1

1. Find the perimeter.

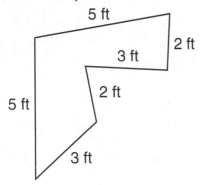

5 ft

2 ft

3 ft

2 ft

5 ft

3 ft

Perimeter = _____
                    (unit)

SRB
132 133

2. Measure to the nearest $\frac{1}{4}$ inch.

_____

_____

Draw a line segment $1\frac{1}{4}$ inches long.

SRB
125 126

3. Solve.

12,469 + 10 = _____

12,469 + 100 = _____

12,469 + 1,000 = _____

12,469 + 10,000 = _____

SRB
18 19

4. Write <, >, or = .

3 decimeters _____ 30 millimeters

$1\frac{1}{2}$ yards _____ 24 inches

45 centimeters _____ 1 meter

9 feet _____ 3 yards

SRB
122 128

5. Circle the names that belong in the box.

| 56 |

100 − 44	93 − 27	33 + 13
86 − 30	8 × 7	26 + 30
46 + 15	20 + 20 + 16	

SRB
14 15

6. What is the total value of the coins?

6 Ⓠ
4 Ⓓ
3 Ⓝ
2 Ⓟ

Total value: $_____

Use with Lesson 4.1.

More Multiplication Number Stories

- Fill in the multiplication/division diagram.
- Make an array with counters. Mark the dots to show the array.
- Find the answer. Write the unit with your answer. Write a number model.

1. Mrs. Kwan has 3 boxes of scented markers. Each box has 8 markers. How many markers does she have?

boxes	markers per box	total number of markers

Answer: _____
(unit)

Number model: _____

---

2. Monica keeps her doll collection in a case with 5 shelves. On each shelf there are 6 dolls. How many dolls are in Monica's collection?

shelves	dolls per shelf	total number of dolls

Answer: _____
(unit)

Number model: _____

---

3. During the summer Jack mows lawns. He can mow 4 lawns per day. How many lawns can he mow in 7 days?

days	lawns per day	total number of lawns

Answer: _____
(unit)

Number model: _____

Perimeter

Measure the perimeter in inches of each figure.

1.

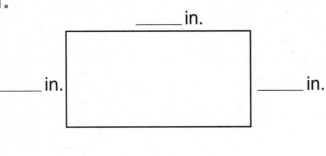

_____ in.

_____ in.   _____ in.

_____ in.

Perimeter: _____ inches

2.

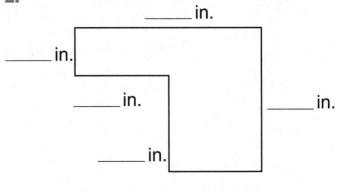

_____ in.

_____ in.

_____ in.   _____ in.

_____ in.

_____ in.

Perimeter: _____ inches

3.

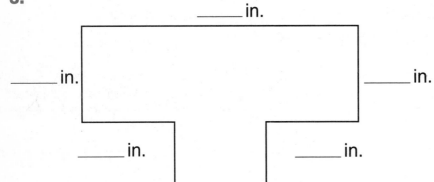

_____ in.

_____ in.   _____ in.

_____ in.

_____ in.   _____ in.

_____ in.

Perimeter: _____ inches

4.

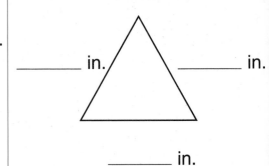

_____ in.   _____ in.

_____ in.

Perimeter: _____ inches

5. Draw any figure with
a perimeter of
20 centimeters.

Use with Lesson 4.2.

Math Boxes 4.2

1. Draw a 2 × 4 rectangle.

Number model: _____ × _____ = _____

Area: _____ square units

 SRB 136–138

2. 10 packs of gum on the shelf in the candy store. 8 sticks of gum per pack.
How many sticks of gum in all?

packs	sticks of gum per pack	total number of sticks of gum

 SRB 191

3. Fill in the numbers.

1,002; 1,001; 1,000; _____;

_____; _____

14,116; 14,117; 14,118; _____;

_____; _____

5,097; 5,098; _____; _____;

_____; _____

4. Fill in the number grid.

2,946

SRB 7 8

5. Put these units of measure in order from smallest to largest.

mile _____

foot _____

yard _____

inch _____

 SRB 128

6. Measure to the nearest centimeter.

_____

_____

Draw a line segment 5 centimeters long.

 SRB 119–121

Division Practice

Use counters to find the answers. Fill in the blanks.

16 cents shared equally

1. by 2 people:	**2.** by 3 people:	**3.** by 4 people:
_____ ¢ per person	_____ ¢ per person	_____ ¢ per person
_____ ¢ remaining	_____ ¢ remaining	_____ ¢ remaining

25¢ shared equally

4. How many people get 5¢?	**5.** How many people get 3¢?	**6.** How many people get 6¢?
_____ people	_____ people	_____ people
_____ ¢ remaining	_____ ¢ remaining	_____ ¢ remaining

30 stamps shared equally

7. by 10 people:	**8.** by 5 people:	**9.** by 6 people:
_____ stamps per person	_____ stamps per person	_____ stamps per person
_____ stamps remaining	_____ stamps remaining	_____ stamps remaining

10. 21 days 7 days per week	**11.** 32 crayons 6 crayons per box	**12.** 24 eggs 6 eggs per row
_____ weeks	_____ boxes of crayons	_____ rows of eggs
_____ days remaining	_____ crayons remaining	_____ eggs remaining

13. There are 18 counters in an array. There are 6 rows.

How many counters are in each row? _____ counters per row

14. Five children share 12 markers equally. How many markers does

each child get? _____ markers   _____ markers remaining

1. Find the perimeter.

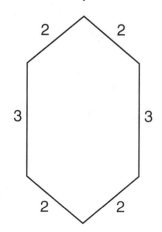

Unit
cm

2   2

3   3

2   2

_____ cm

This shape is a

_____.

SRB
94 95
132 133

2. Make a 4-by-4 array. Complete the number model.

```
· · · · · ·
· · · · · ·
· · · · · ·
· · · · · ·
· · · · · ·
```

_____ × _____ = _____

SRB
63 64

3. Solve.

$45{,}582 - 10 =$ _____

$45{,}582 + 100 =$ _____

$45{,}582 + 1{,}000 =$ _____

$45{,}582 - 10{,}000 =$ _____

SRB
18 19

4. Put these metric units of measure in order from smallest to largest.

centimeter _____

kilometer _____

millimeter _____

meter _____

SRB
122

5. Draw the hands to show 10:20.

How many minutes

until 11:10? _____

6. Complete.

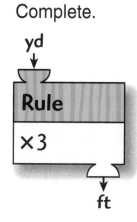

yd	ft
2	
5	
	9
	30

Rule

×3

SRB
179 180

Solving Multiplication and Division Number Stories

Solve each number story. Use counters, draw an array, or do whatever helps you find the answer. Fill in the diagrams and write number models.

1. Robert has 3 packages of pencils. There are 12 pencils in each package. How many pencils does Robert have in all?

   Answer: _____
   (unit)

   Number model: _____

packages	pencils per package	total number of pencils

2. Robert gives 3 pencils to each of his friends. How many friends will get 3 pencils each?

   Answer: _____
   (unit)

   Number model: _____

friends	pencils per friend	total number of pencils

3. What if Robert shares his pencils equally among himself and 11 friends? How many pencils does each child get?

   Answer: _____
   (unit)

   Number model: _____

Robert and friends	pencils per friend	total number of pencils

4. A class of 30 children wants to play ball. How many teams can be made with exactly 6 children on each team?

   Answer: _____
   (unit)

   Number model: _____

teams	children per team	total number of children

5. The same class of 30 children wants to have exactly 4 children on each team. How many teams can be made?

   Answer: _____
   (unit)

   Number model: _____

teams	children per team	total number of children

Use with Lesson 4.4.

Math Boxes 4.4

1. Draw a shape with an area of 9 square centimeters.

SRB
136–138

2. Draw an array and complete a number model to match the diagram.

packs	cards per pack	total number of cards
3	6	?

Number model: _____

SRB
63 64
191 192

3. Fill in the rule and the empty frames.

+10

| 117 | | 121 | | 125 |

SRB
176 177

4. Scientists studying green turtles counted 136 eggs in a clutch of eggs. 87 eggs did not hatch.

How many eggs did hatch?

_____ eggs

SRB
190

5. Add. Show your work.

| **Unit** |
| |

478
+ 236

309
+ 2,047

SRB
51 52

6. Write <, >, or =.

3 + 8 + 7 _____ 4 + 8 + 6

7 + 7 + 9 _____ 9 + 9 + 5

9 + 1 + 8 _____ 11 + 5 + 3

8 + 8 + 8 _____ 15 + 5 + 7

5 + 35 + 17 _____ 15 + 18 + 25

SRB
13

Math Boxes 4.5

1. Use counters to solve.

Some children are sharing
22 marbles equally. Each child
gets 6 marbles.

How many children are sharing?

_____
(unit)

How many marbles are left over?

_____
(unit)

2. Draw Xs in a 5-by-9 array.

How many Xs? _____

Write a number model for the array.

_____

3. Subtract. Show your work.

Unit

$$\begin{array}{r} 406 \\ -\ 46 \\ \hline \end{array} \qquad \begin{array}{r} 5{,}168 \\ -\ 2{,}936 \\ \hline \end{array}$$

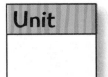

4. Add.

_____ = 47 + 192

_____ = 147 + 292

_____ = 247 + 392

5. Fill in the unit box.
Write the missing
number in the diagram.

Unit

Start	Change	End
	+107	392

Write a number model.

_____ + _____ = _____

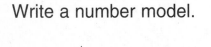

6. Measure to the nearest $\frac{1}{4}$ inch.

_____

_____

Draw a line segment 3 inches long.

Math Boxes 4.6

1. On the centimeter grid below, draw a shape with an area of 12 square centimeters.

SRB
136–138

2. Write a multiplication story by filling in the blanks.

8 rows of _____

6 _____ in each row

How many _____ in all?

Write a number model.

_____

SRB
65   66

3. Solve.

$2 \times 9 = $ _____

$4 \times 0 = $ _____

_____ $= 66 \times 1$

$7 \times$ _____ $= 70$

_____ $= 5 \times 8$

SRB
46   47

4. Write the number sixteen thousand, three hundred two.

_____

Write the words for 12,015.

_____

_____

SRB
18–20

5. Justin bought 2 gallons of milk. Each gallon cost $2.79. He paid with a $10 bill. How much change did he receive?

_____

SRB
188–190

6. Find the perimeter of the trapezoid.

2.5 cm

2.5 cm   2.5 cm

4.5 cm

Perimeter: _____
                    (unit)

SRB
132 133

Math Boxes 4.7

1. Make equal groups.

30 days

make _____ weeks

with _____ days left over.

56 pennies

make _____ quarters

with _____ pennies left over.

 68

2. Draw a 3-by-6 array.

What is the number model?

_____ × _____ = _____

 63 64

3. Solve.

$2 \times 2 =$ _____

$16 = 4 \times$ _____

$3 \times 4 =$ _____

$5 \times 6 =$ _____

$18 =$ _____ $\times 3$

$7 \times 4 =$ _____

 46 47

4. Write the ×, ÷ fact family for the numbers 3, 8, and 24.

$24 =$ _____ $\times$ _____

$24 =$ _____ $\times$ _____

_____ $= 24 \div$ _____

_____ $=$ _____ $\div$ _____

 48 49

5. Add. Show your work.

Unit

```
  881          6,709
+ 746          +  448
```

 51 52

6. There are 46 trees and 25 flowers. How many more trees are there than flowers?

_____ trees

Write a number model.

_____

 190

How Many Dots?

Materials ❑ square pattern blocks

❑ calculator

1. Estimate how many dots are in the array at the right.

   About _____ dots

Make another estimate.
Follow these steps:

2. Cover part of the array with a square pattern block. About how many dots can you cover with one block?

   _____ dots

3. Cover the array. Use as many square pattern blocks as you can. Do not go over the borders of the array. How many blocks did you use?

   _____ blocks

4. Use the information in Steps 2 and 3 to estimate the total number of dots in the array. About _____ dots

---

Challenge

5. Try to find the exact number of dots in the array. Use a calculator to help you. Total number of dots = _____ .

Follow-Up

Describe how you found the exact number of dots. _____

_____

_____

Setting up Chairs

1. Record the answer to the problem about setting up chairs from *Math Masters*, page 52.

   There were _____ chairs in the room.

2. Circle dots below to show how the chairs were set up for each of the clues.

Rows of 2	Rows of 3	Rows of 4	Rows of 5
• •	• • •	• • • •	• • • • •
• •	• • •	• • • •	• • • • •
• •	• • •	• • • •	• • • • •
• •	• • •	• • • •	• • • • •
• •	• • •	• • • •	• • • • •
• •	• • •	• • • •	• • • • •
• •	• • •	• • • •	• • • • •
• •	• • •	• • • •	• • • • •
• •	• • •	• • • •	• • • • •
• •	• • •	• • • •	• • • • •
• •	• • •	• • • •	• • • • •
• •	• • •	• • • •	• • • • •
• •	• • •	• • • •	• • • • •
• •	• • •	• • • •	• • • • •
• •	• • •	• • • •	• • • • •
• 1 left over	• 1 left over	• 1 left over	0 left over

Math Boxes 4.8

1. Measure to the nearest centimeter.

_____

_____

Draw a line segment 6 centimeters long.

SRB
119–121

2. Complete.

_____ days in a week

_____ days in two weeks

_____ days in three weeks

_____ days in four weeks

SRB
271

3. Solve.

$2 \times 7 =$ _____

$8 \times 0 =$ _____

_____ $= 24 \times 1$

$5 \times$ _____ $= 50$

_____ $= 5 \times 5$

SRB
46 47

4. Complete.

20 dimes $= \$$_____

20 nickels $= \$$_____

20 quarters $= \$$_____

10 quarters and 7 dimes $=$

$\$$_____

5. Subtract. Show your work.

Unit

$$\begin{array}{r} 904 \\ -\ 368 \\ \hline \end{array} \qquad \begin{array}{r} 731 \\ -\ 53 \\ \hline \end{array}$$

SRB
54 55

6. Add.

$15 + 15 + 13 =$ _____

$34 + 16 + 12 =$ _____

$23 + 13 + 17 =$ _____

$21 + 14 + 19 =$ _____

Estimating Distances

Locations to Visit

1. Mt. St. Helens
2. Disneyland
3. Yellowstone National Park
4. Pike's Peak
5. Sears Tower

6. Civil Rights Memorial
7. Statue of Liberty
8. White House
9. Cowboy Hall of Fame
10. Space Shuttle Launch Site, Cape Canaveral

Map Scale

0 ⊢──────┤ 300 miles

Use with Lesson 4.9.

A Pretend Trip

Pretend you want to take a trip to see some of the sights in the United States. Find out about how far it is between locations.

1. The Statue of Liberty is number _____.

    The Sears Tower is number _____.

    The distance between them is about _____ inches on the map.

    That is about _____ miles.

2. Pike's Peak is number _____.

    The White House is number _____.

    The distance between them is about _____ inches on the map.

    That is about _____ miles.

3. Yellowstone National Park is number _____.

    The Cowboy Hall of Fame is number _____.

    The distance between them is about _____ inches on the map.

    That is about _____ miles.

4. The Civil Rights Memorial is number _____.

    Disneyland is number _____.

    The distance between them is about _____ inches on the map.

    That is about _____ miles.

5. Make up one of your own.

    _____ is number _____.

    _____ is number _____.

    The distance between them is about _____ inches on the map.

    That is about _____ miles.

Math Boxes 4.9

1. Use counters to solve.

18 marbles are shared equally.
Each child gets 5 marbles.
How many children are sharing?

_____
(unit)

How many marbles are left over?

_____
(unit)

67

2. Draw an array of 28 Xs arranged in 4 rows.

How many Xs in each row? _____
Write a number model for the array.

_____

63 64

3. Solve.

$3 \times$ _____ $= 9$

_____ $= 4 \times 5$

$2 \times 6 =$ _____

$35 = 7 \times$ _____

$4 \times 6 =$ _____

$8 =$ _____ $\times 2$

46 47

4. Complete the Fact Triangle.
Write the fact family.

_____ $\times$ _____ $=$ _____

_____ $\times$ _____ $=$ _____

_____ $\div$ _____ $=$ _____

_____ $\div$ _____ $=$ _____

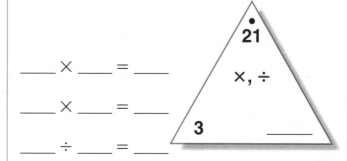

21

×, ÷

3   _____

48 49

5. Solve. Each square equals 1 sq cm.

Area: _____ square centimeters

136–138

6. Complete.

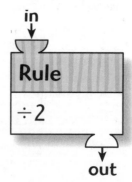

in
Rule
÷ 2
out

in	out
8	
16	
	10
50	

179 180

1. 56,937

Which digit is in the
tens place? _3_

Which digit is in the
thousands place? ____

Which digit is in the
hundreds place? ____

Which digit is in the
ones place? ____

2. Put these numbers in order from
smallest to largest.

4,073   47,003   43,700   7,430

_____ _____ _____ _____

↑   ↑
smallest   largest

3. Write the number that has

5 hundreds

7 thousands

8 ones

4 tens

2 ten-thousands

_____

Read it to a partner.

4. Which is more?

$3.45 or $3.09 _____

$0.34 or $0.09 _____

$14.50 or $14.55 _____

5. Solve.

```
  6,000        400
    300          9
     20      8,000
+     8     +    30
_____     _____
```

6. Write the number that is 100 more.

76 _____

300 _____

471 _____

8,634 _____

5,925 _____

Place-Value Review

Follow the steps to find each number in Problems 1 and 2.

1. Write 6 in the ones place.
   Write 4 in the thousands place.
   Write 9 in the hundreds place.
   Write 0 in the tens place.
   Write 1 in the ten-thousands place.

2. Write 6 in the tens place.
   Write 4 in the ten-thousands place.
   Write 9 in the ones place.
   Write 0 in the hundreds place.
   Write 1 in the thousands place.

   _____ _____ , _____ _____ _____   _____ _____ , _____ _____ _____

3. Compare the two numbers you wrote in Problems 1 and 2.

   Which is greater? _____

4. Complete.
   The 9 in 4,965 stands for 9 _____*hundreds*_____ or ___*900*___.

   The 7 in 87,629 stands for 7_____ or _____.

   The 4 in 48,215 stands for 4_____ or _____.

   The 0 in 72,601 stands for 0_____ or _____.

Continue the counts.

5. 4,707; 4,708; 4,709; _____; _____; _____

6. 7,697; 7,698; 7,699; _____; _____; _____

7. 903; 902; 901; _____; _____; _____

8. 6,004; 6,003; 6,002; _____; _____; _____

9. 47,265; 47,266; 47,267; _____; _____; _____

Write the number that is 1,000 more.

10. 6,583 _____   11. 9,990 _____   12. 39,510 _____

Write the number that is 1,000 less.

13. 6,583 _____   14. 9,990 _____   15. 20,000 _____

1. 13 crayons are shared equally among 3 children.

How many crayons does each child get? _____
(unit)

How many crayons are left over?

_____
(unit)

2. If a map scale shows that 1 inch represents 200 miles, then

2 inches represents _____ miles

3 inches represents _____ miles

5 inches represents _____ miles

7 inches represents _____ miles

3. Fill in the unit box. Then multiply.

Unit

$2 \times 5 =$ _____

$7 \times 3 =$ _____

_____ $= 5 \times 5$

_____ $= 2 \times 7$

_____ $= 4 \times 6$

4. Complete the number-grid puzzles.

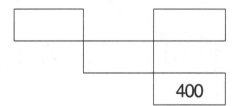

98		

		400

5. Draw a figure with a perimeter of 12 centimeters.

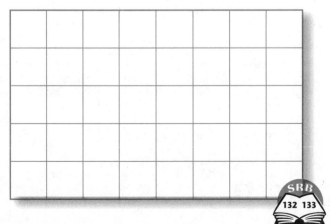

6. The "about 3 times" circle rule:
For any circle, the circumference is about 3 times the diameter.

Unit
inches

diameter	circumference
8	
10	
50	

1. Write the number. This number has

7 thousands

8 tens

5 ten-thousands

1 one

0 hundreds

___ ___,___ ___ ___

SRB 18 19

2. Complete the Fact Triangle and write the fact family.

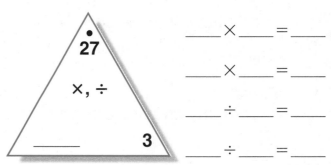

___ × ___ = ___

___ × ___ = ___

___ ÷ ___ = ___

___ ÷ ___ = ___

SRB 48 49

3. Draw a 4 × 6 rectangle.

Number model: ___ × ___ = _____

Area: _____ square units

SRB 136–138

4. Write a multiplication story by filling in the blanks.

8 rows.

5 _____ in each row.

How many in all? _____

Write a number model.

_____

SRB 63 64

5. Fill in the rule and then the empty frames.

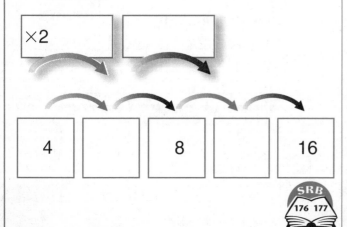

×2

4   8   16

SRB 176 177

6. Fill in the unit box. Write the missing number in the diagram. Write a number model.

_____

Total	
426	
Part	**Part**
285	

Unit

SRB 188 189

1. Write $<$, $>$, or $=$.

263,473 _____ 263,107

37,261 _____ 37,621

99,999 _____ 111,111

Make up your own.

_____ ☐ _____

SRB
13

2. If a map scale shows that 1 cm represents 1,000 km, then

2 cm represents _____ km

9 cm represents _____ km

16 cm represents _____ km

20 cm represents _____ km

SRB
164

3. Fill in the unit box.
Then multiply.

Unit

$5 \times 3 =$ _____

_____ $= 4 \times 5$

$3 \times 3 =$ _____

_____ $= 7 \times 3$

_____ $= 5 \times 5$

SRB
46 47

4. On Tuesday Gabriela put $76 in her bank account. Now she has $123. How much money did she have in her bank account on Monday?

$_____

SRB
190

5.

Days of Indoor Recess

What is the median number of days

of indoor recess? _____ days

SRB
74 82

6. Measure to the nearest $\frac{1}{4}$ inch.

_____

_____

Draw a line segment $2\frac{1}{4}$ inches long.

SRB
125–127

Working with Populations

10 U.S. Cities with the Largest Populations		
	1980*	1995*
New York, NY	7,071,639	7,380,906
Los Angeles, CA	2,968,528	3,553,638
Chicago, IL	3,005,072	2,721,547
Houston, TX	1,611,382	1,744,058
Philadelphia, PA	1,688,210	1,478,002
San Diego, CA	875,538	1,171,121
Phoenix, AZ	790,183	1,159,014
San Antonio, TX	785,940	1,067,816
Dallas, TX	1,007,618	1,053,292
Detroit, MI	1,027,974	1,000,272

*U.S. Census data

Use this table to solve the problems.

1. List the cities that gained population from 1980 to 1995.

    _____

    _____

2. List the cities that lost population from 1980 to 1995.

    _____

3. Look at your answers to Problem 1. Name a city where the population increased by

    a. more than 100,000   b. about 100,000   c. less than 100,000

    _____   _____   _____

4. In 1980, which two cities had a population about half that of

    Houston, TX? _____

5. In 1995, which city had a population about double that of

    Philadelphia, PA? _____

6. Which city had the smallest change in population? _____

108 (one hundred eight)   Use with Lesson 5.4.

Math Boxes 5.4

1. For the number 5,749,862

the 4 means _**40,000**_

the 5 means _____

the 8 means _____

the 7 means _____

the 9 means _____

18 19

2. Complete the Fact Triangle and write the fact family.

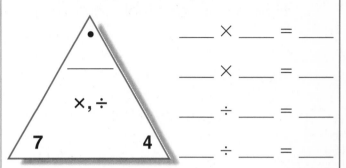

_____ × _____ = _____

_____ × _____ = _____

_____ ÷ _____ = _____

_____ ÷ _____ = _____

48 49

3. Find the perimeter.

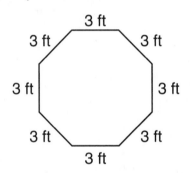

3 ft
3 ft   3 ft
3 ft   3 ft
3 ft   3 ft
3 ft

Perimeter = _____
(unit)

132 133

4. Teesha has 345 marbles. Keiko has 279 marbles. How many fewer marbles does Keiko have than Teesha?

_____ marbles

190

5. Write a division story by filling in the blanks.
There are 48 _____ in 6 rows.

How many _____ are

in each row? _____

Write a number model.

_____

68

6. Measure to the nearest centimeter.

_____

_____

Draw a line segment 4.5 centimeters long.

119–121

How Old Am I?

1. On what date were you born? _____

2. How old were you on your last birthday? _____ years old

3. About how many minutes old do you think you were on your last birthday? Make an X next to your guess.

_____ between 10,000 and 100,000 minutes

_____ between 100,000 and 1,000,000 minutes

_____ between 1,000,000 and 10,000,000 minutes

Use your calculator.

4. a. About how many days old were you on your last birthday? Do not include any leap year days.   _____

   b. That's about how many hours?   _____

   c. That's about how many minutes?   _____

Challenge

Adding Leap Year Days

5. a. List all of the leap years from the time you were born to your last birthday.   _____

   b. That adds how many extra days to your last birthday?   _____

   c. How many extra minutes?   _____

6. Add the number of extra minutes to the number of minutes in your answer in Problem 4c. How many minutes are there in all?   _____

7. On my last birthday, I was about _____ minutes old.

110 (one hundred ten)

Math Boxes 5.5

---

1. Circle the largest number.
Underline the smallest number.

1,099,999

697,432

697,500

697,490

1,110,000

697,433

 SRB 20

---

2. If a map scale shows that 1 in. represents 50 miles, then

_____ in. represents 200 miles

_____ in. represents 300 miles

9 in. represents _____ miles

11 in. represents _____ miles

 SRB 164

---

3. Circle the number that is about 10,000 less than 30,000.

56,023   21,004

35,900   15,999

SRB 18 19

---

4. Fill in the unit box. Then multiply.

$4 \times 3 =$ _____

$2 \times 7 =$ _____

_____ $= 5 \times 7$

_____ $= 2 \times 5$

_____ $= 6 \times 5$

Unit

 SRB 46 47

---

5. Body-plus-tail lengths (inches) for 13 cats:

30, 29, 28, 24, 29, 35, 16, 27, 29, 36, 28, 31, 32

Median = _____

Maximum = _____

 SRB 73 74

---

6. Draw a shape with an area of 16 square units.

How many sides does your shape have? _____ sides

 SRB 94 95 136–138

Finding the Value of Base-10 Blocks

Materials ❑ classroom supply of base-10 blocks

Work in a group.

1. Estimate the value of the base-10 blocks. Don't let anyone in your group see your estimate.

   Estimate: _____

2. Plan how your group will find the actual value of the blocks and what each person will do to help. Then carry out your plan. Describe your job.

   _____

   _____

3. What is the actual value of the base-10 blocks? _____

4. Write the estimates of your group and the actual value of the base-10 blocks in order from smallest to largest. Circle the actual value of the base-10 blocks.

   _____

   _____

5. a. Which estimate was closest to the actual value? _____

   b. How many estimates were higher than the closest estimate? _____

   c. How many estimates were lower than the closest estimate? _____

   d. How far was the highest estimate from the actual value? _____

   e. How far was the lowest estimate from the actual value? _____

6. How does your estimate compare to the actual value? _____

7. If you have extra time, put part of the block supply to the side.

   First estimate its value and then find its actual value.

Use with Lesson 5.6.

Squares, Rectangles, and Triangles

Materials   ☐ straightedge

A •

H •   • E

D •   • B

G •   • F

•
C

Work on your own or with a partner.

1. Use your straightedge to draw line segments between points
   A and *B*, *B* and *C*, *C* and *D*, and *D* and *A*.

   What kind of shape did you draw? _____

2. Now draw line segments between points *E* and *F*, *F* and *G*,
   G and *H*, and *H* and *E*.

   What kind of shape did you draw? _____

3. Draw line segments between points *E* and *G* and between points
   F and *H*.

   How many different sizes of squares are there? _____

   How many squares in all? _____

4. How many different sizes of triangles are there? _____

   How many triangles in all? _____

5. How many rectangles are there that are not squares? _____

Pattern-Block Perimeters

Materials ❑ pattern blocks: square, large rhombus, small rhombus, triangle

Work on your own or with a partner.

1. Imagine that each polygon is "rolled" along a line, starting at point *S*. Estimate the distance each polygon will "roll" after 1 full turn. Mark an X at the point you think the polygon will reach.

2. Check your estimate by "rolling" a pattern block that matches the polygon. Circle the point reached by the pattern block.

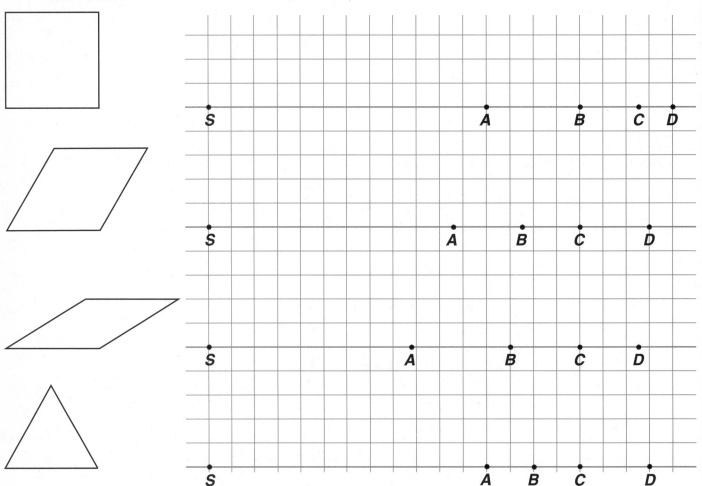

3. Which 3 shapes have about the same perimeter?

   _____

4. Which of these 3 shapes do you think has the largest area? _____

5. Which of the 4 shapes do you think has the smallest area? _____

Use with Lesson 5.6.

Math Boxes 5.6

1. In the number 6,940,173

the 9 means _900,000_

the 6 means _____

the 1 means _____

the 4 means _____

the 7 means _____

SRB
18 19

2. Complete the number-grid puzzle.

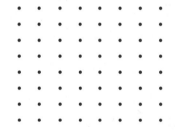

8,742

SRB
7 8

3. Use your calculator.

Enter	Change to	How?
894	12,894	
1,366	966	
627,581	628,581	
43,775	43,175	

SRB
18 19

4. Draw a 7-by-6 array.

What is the number model?

___ × ___ = _____

SRB
63 64

5. Fill in the rule and then fill in the empty frames.

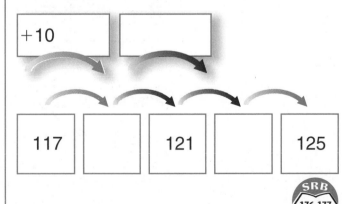

+10

117   ____   121   ____   125

SRB
176 177

6. Add.

```
        72
  28   407
 374   283
+101  + 19
```

SRB
51–53

Place Value in Decimals

If the grid is ONE, then which part of each grid is shaded?

Write a decimal and a fraction below each grid.

1.

2.

3.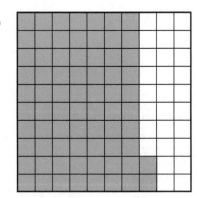

fraction: _____

decimal: _____

fraction: _____

decimal: _____

fraction: _____

decimal: _____

Place Value in Decimals (cont.)

4. Which decimal in each pair is greater? Use the grids in Exercises 1–3 to help you.

0.5 or 0.08 _____ 0.08 or 0.72 _____ 0.5 or 0.72 _____

Color part of each grid to show the decimal named.

5. Color 0.7 of the grid.

6. Color 0.07 of the grid.

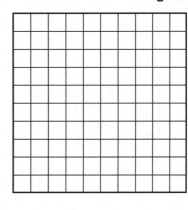

7. Color 0.46 of the grid.

8. Write 0.7, 0.07, and 0.46 in order from smallest to largest.

Use the grids in Exercises 5–7 to help you. _____ _____ _____

Challenge

Color part of each grid to show the fraction named.

9. Color $\frac{4}{10}$ of the grid.

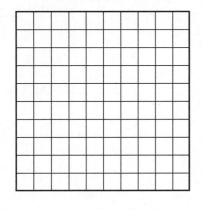

10. Color $\frac{1}{2}$ of the grid.

11. Color $\frac{23}{100}$ of the grid.

12. Write $\frac{23}{100}$ as a decimal. _____

Math Boxes 5.7

1. Circle the largest number.
Underline the smallest number.

2,999,999

946,487

946,800

946,793

4,000,007

946,200

2. If a map scale shows that 1 cm represents 25 miles, then

_____ cm represents 125 miles

_____ cm represents 200 miles

_____ cm represents 375 miles

20 cm represents _____ miles

3. Solve.

Double 2 _____

Double 10 _____

Double 75 _____

Double 1,000 _____

Double 1,500 _____

4. Fill in the unit box.
Then multiply.

Unit

$4 \times 5 =$ _____

$2 \times 6 =$ _____

$3 \times 5 =$ _____

_____ $= 7 \times 4$

_____ $= 6 \times 5$

5. Ages of 9 teachers:

30, 24, 49, 50, 38, 44, 40, 35, 51

Median = _____

Maximum = _____

6. Find the perimeter.

Unit
yards

Perimeter: _____
(unit)

Exploring Decimals

A	B		C	D
_27_ hundredths	_2_ tenths, _7_ hundredths		0. _27_	$\frac{27}{100}$
_____ hundredths	_____ tenths, _____ hundredths		0. _____	
_____ hundredths	_____ tenths, _____ hundredths		0. _____	
_____ hundredths	_____ tenths, _____ hundredths		0. _____	
_____ hundredths	_____ tenths, _____ hundredths		0. _____	
_____ hundredths	_____ tenths, _____ hundredths		0. _____	
_____ hundredths	_____ tenths, _____ hundredths		0. _____	

Use with Lesson 5.8.   (one hundred nineteen) **119**

Math Boxes 5.8

1. For the number 4,963,521

4 means $\underline{4,000,000}$

3 means _____

1 means _____

6 means _____

9 means _____

2. If each grid is ONE, what part of each grid is shaded? Write the decimal.

_____   _____

3. Solve.

$$
\begin{array}{r} 3{,}976 \\ -\ 1{,}439 \\ \hline \end{array}
\qquad
\begin{array}{r} 6{,}840 \\ -\ 5{,}695 \\ \hline \end{array}
$$

$$
\begin{array}{r} 14{,}256 \\ -\ 3{,}661 \\ \hline \end{array}
$$

4. How many slices does each person get if 64 slices of pizza are shared equally among 4 people?

Answer: _____
                    (unit)

Number model:

_____

5. Draw a 3 × 7 rectangle.

Number model: ___ × ___ = _____

Area: _____ square units

6. Draw the hands to show 5:50.

How long until 8:30?

_____ hours _____ minutes

Decimals for Metric Measurements

1. Fill in the missing information. Put longs and cubes end to end on a meterstick to help you.

Length in Centimeters	Number of Longs	Number of Cubes	Length in Meters
24 cm	2	4	0.24 m
36 cm	_____	_____	_____ m
_____ cm	0	3	_____ m
8 cm	_____	_____	_____ m
_____ cm	_____	_____	0.3 m
_____ cm	4	3	_____ m

Work with a partner. Each partner uses base-10 blocks to make one length in each pair. Compare the lengths and circle the one that is greater.

2. 0.18 or 0.5

3. 0.2 or 0.08

4. 0.09 or 0.12

5. 0.24 or 0.42

6. 0.10 or 0.02

7. 0.3 or 0.24

Follow these directions on the ruler below.

8. Make a dot at 4 cm and label it with the letter *A*.

9. Make a dot at 0.1 m and label it with the letter *B*.

10. Make a dot at 0.15 m and label it with the letter *C*.

11. Make a dot at 0.08 m and label it with the letter *D*.

Math Boxes 5.9

1. Put these numbers in order from smallest to largest.

998,752 _____

1,000,008 _____

750,999 _____

1,709,832 _____

2. Write the number that has

2 in the ones place

6 in the tenths place

7 in the hundredths place

_____ • _____ _____

3. Solve.

Double 6 _____

Double 24 _____

Double 59 _____

Double 113 _____

Double 642 _____

4. Fill in the unit box. Then multiply.

Unit

_____ = 3 × 3

_____ = 4 × 6

5 × 5 = _____

3 × 6 = _____

2 × 4 = _____

5. Median number of books read? _____

Maximum number of books

read? _____

6. 7 boxes. 7 cans per box.

How many cans in all?

_____ cans

9 cars. 3 people per car.

How many people in all?

_____ people

How Wet? How Dry?

1. Use the scale at the left and the map on page 245 of the *Student Reference Book.* Make a dot for the level of precipitation in each of the following cities: Phoenix, Helena, Denver, Cleveland, and Asheville. Write the name of the city next to the dot.

2. Which city gets about 2 centimeters less rain than New York?

_____

3. Which city gets about half as much rain as Denver?

_____

4. Which city gets about 5 times as much rain as Helena?

_____

5. A decimeter is 10 centimeters. Which cities on the map get at least 1 decimeter of rain?

_____

_____

Did You Know?

According to the National Geographic Society, the rainiest place in the world is Mount Waialeale in Hawaii. It rains an average of about 1,170 centimeters a year on Mount Waialeale.

Challenge

6. Suppose it rained 1,170 centimeters in your classroom. Would the water reach the ceiling?

_____ millimeters = 1,170 centimeters = _____ meters

Answer: _____

Math Boxes 5.10

1. Complete the Frames and Arrows.

| 1 | | 8 | | |

SRB
176 177

2. Color 0.6 of the grid.

SRB
33 34

3. Complete.

2 hours = _____ minutes

5 weeks = _____ days

3 hours = _____ minutes

2 years = _____ days

SRB
156 157

4. Circle any measurements in Column B that match the one in Column A.

Column A	Column B	
2 feet	12 in.	3 yd
	24 in.	1 yd
3 feet	36 in.	1 m
	1 yd	30 in.
2 yards	50 in.	72 in.
	6 ft	9 ft

SRB
128

5. Add.

```
     3            3
    96           33
   104          333
 + 327       + 3,333
```

SRB
51–53

6. Complete.

in
↓

Rule

÷ 3

out

in	out
9	
15	
	7
	10

SRB
179 180

More Decimals

Use your place-value tool to help you.

Write the number that matches each description.

1. 4 in the tenths place

    2 in the thousandths place

    7 in the hundredths place

    0 in the ones place

    _____

2. 5 in the tenths place

    3 in the tens place

    5 in the ones place

    3 in the hundredths place

    _____

3. 4 in the thousandths place

    2 in the ones place

    7 in the hundredths place

    0 in the tenths place

    _____

4. 0 in the hundredths place

    6 in the ones place

    8 in the thousandths place

    0 in the tenths place

    _____

5. With your partner, decide how to read each of the decimals in Problems 1–4.

Write each number below as a decimal.

6. nine-tenths _____

7. thirty-thousandths _____

8. fifty-three hundredths _____

9. sixty and four-tenths _____

10. seven and seven-thousandths _____

11. sixty and four-hundredths _____

12. eight hundred _____

13. sixty-two thousandths _____

Fill in the missing numbers.

Unit
meter

14.

0 ____ ____ ____ ____ ____ ____ ____ ____ ____ 1

15.

0 ____ ____ ____ ____ ____ ____ ____ ____ ____ 0.1

Math Boxes 5.11

1. How much of this grid is shaded?

_____ • _____ _____

33 34

2. Write the number that has

4 in the tenths place

0 in the hundredths place

6 in the ones place

9 in the thousandths place

_____ • _____ _____ _____

35

3. Circle the number that is about 1 million less than 6 million.

50,023

6,900,800

4,986,500

3,090,222

18 19

4. Fill in the unit box. Then multiply.

Unit

$3 \times 5 =$ _____

$4 \times 6 =$ _____

_____ $= 7 \times 5$

_____ $= 4 \times 4$

_____ $= 6 \times 3$

46 47

5. Draw a 4-by-9 array of Xs.

How many Xs in all? _____
Write a number model.

_____

63 64

6. True or false? Circle one.

The line segment is 6.2 centimeters long.

true   false

_____

119–121

Use with Lesson 5.11.

Math Boxes 5.12

---

1. Solve.

16 + 9 = _____

16 + 90 = _____

16 + 900 = _____

16 + 9,000 = _____

16 + 90,000 = _____

2. Color 0.08 of the grid.

SRB
33 34

---

3. Find the differences between these high and low temperatures.

	High	Low	Difference
Pittsburgh	92°F	66°F	
Tempe	102°F	88°F	
Detroit	29°F	17°F	
Charlotte	37°F	23°F	

SRB
152–154

4. True or false? Circle one.

The line segment is 4.6 centimeters long.

true   false

_____

SRB
119–121

---

5. Add. Look for easy combinations.

25 + 13 + 5 = _____

19 + 11 + 23 = _____

33 + 14 + 27 = _____

6. Write the number that has

6 in the ones place

4 in the tenths place

3 in the hundredths place

2 in the thousandths place

_____ • _____ _____ _____

SRB
35

Math Boxes 5.13

1. Draw line segments *AB* and *CD*.

A•   •B

C•

                    •D

SRB
88

2. Complete.

A triangle has _____ sides and

_____ angles.

A quadrangle has _____ sides and

_____ angles.

SRB
96 97

3. Draw a quadrangle.

SRB
98

4. Draw a polygon.

SRB
94

5. Circle the shape that has line symmetry.

SRB
111 112

6. Circle the pictures that show 3-dimensional shapes.

SRB
102 103

Line Segments, Rays, and Lines

1. Write S next to each line segment. Write R next to each ray.
   Write L next to each line.

Points *D, T, Q,* and *M* are marked. Use a straightedge to draw the following.

2. Draw $\overline{QT}$. Draw $\vec{DT}$. Draw $\overleftrightarrow{MQ}$.

D.   .T

M.   .Q

Draw a line segment between
each pair of points. How many line
segments did you draw?

Example

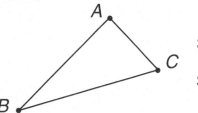

3 points

3 line segments

3.   P.

   A.

          .L

    U .

   4 points

   _____ line segments

4.   R.

   O.

                .E

        S.

            . I

   5 points

   _____ line segments

1. Use the "about 3 times" circle rule to complete the table below:
For any circle, the circumference is about 3 times the diameter.

Unit
centimeters

diameter	circumference
	12
	18
	27

SRB
134 135

2. In the number 2.673

the 6 means ___6 tenths___

the 3 means _____

the 7 means _____

the 2 means _____

SRB
35

3. Fill in the unit box. Then divide.

Unit

$30 \div 6 =$ _____

$12 \div 4 =$ _____

$20 \div 5 =$ _____

_____ $= 14 \div 7$

_____ $= 9 \div 3$

SRB
46 47

4. Write 4 division names for 6.

6

SRB
14 15
46 47

5. Write $<$, $>$, or $=$.

0.65 _____ 0.56

0.07 _____ 0.7

0.098 _____ 0.102

73.4 _____ 75.2

SRB
36

6. Solve.

$15 - 9 =$ _____

$25 - 9 =$ _____

$55 - 9 =$ _____

$85 - 9 =$ _____

$105 - 9 =$ _____

Geometry Hunt

parallel line segments

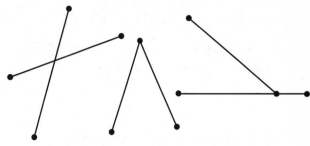

intersecting line segments

Part 1

Look for things in the classroom or hallway that are parallel.
Look for things that intersect. List these things below or draw
a few of each of them on another sheet of paper.

Parallel

_____

_____

_____

Intersecting

_____

_____

_____

Part 2

Look for things in the classroom or hallway that have one or more right angles.
List these things below or draw a few of them on another sheet of paper.

_____

_____

_____

Math Boxes 6.2

1. Draw a ray, $\overrightarrow{AB}$. Draw a line segment, $\overline{CD}$. Draw a line, $\overleftrightarrow{EF}$.

• A   • B

• C   • D

• E   • F

SRB 88 89

2. Complete.

Unit

Total		
Part	**Part**	**Part**
217	197	300

Number model:

_____

SRB 188 189

3. Complete the Fact Triangle. Write the fact family.

_____

_____

_____

72

×, ÷

8   _____

SRB 48 49

4. Complete.

in	out
16	
	240
225	
133	
	1,000

in

Rule

double

out

SRB 179 180

5. What is the difference in points between Players B and C?

_____ points

What are the total points scored for all players?

_____ points

SRB 80 81

6. Write equivalent lengths.

$\frac{1}{3}$ yd = _____ ft

18 in. = _____ yd

50 mm = _____ cm

0.6 m = _____ cm

SRB 122 128 129

Turns

Use your connected straws to show each turn.
Draw a picture of what you did.
Draw a curved arrow to show the direction of the turn.

Example

right $\frac{1}{4}$ turn (clockwise)	1. right $\frac{1}{2}$ turn (clockwise)	2. left $\frac{1}{4}$ turn (counterclockwise)
3. left $\frac{3}{4}$ turn (counterclockwise)	4. right $\frac{3}{4}$ turn (clockwise)	5. left $\frac{1}{2}$ turn (counterclockwise)

Math Boxes 6.3

---

1. Circle the pair of lines that are parallel.

91

2. Annette had $16.75 in her purse. She spent $8.66 at the store. How much money does she have left?

_____

190

---

3. Write <, >, or =.

4×7 _____ 5×6

7×5 _____ 6×3

4×6 _____ 5×5

5×7 _____ 4×9

13
46 47

4. Solve.

$4{,}695 + 1{,}013 =$ _____

$5{,}692 - 3{,}688 =$ _____

_____ $= 10{,}000 + 695$

SRB
51 52
54 55

---

5. Complete.

SRB
176 177

6. Rectangle *ABCD* is a(n)

_____ by _____ rectangle.

The area of rectangle *ABCD*:

_____ $\times$ _____ $=$ _____ square units.

136–138

Use with Lesson 6.3.

Triangle Explorations

Part 1

Follow these steps:

1. Mark three points on the circle.

2. Label them *A, B,* and *C.*

3. Use a straightedge to connect each pair of points with a line segment.

4. What figure have you drawn?

    _____

Part 2

Write all six 3-letter names that are possible for your triangle.
The first letter of each name is given below.

___A___   ___A___   ___B___   ___B___   ___C___   ___C___

Part 3

Work with a group.

Make triangles with straws and twist-ties. Make at least one of each of
the following kinds of triangles:

- all 3 sides the same length
- only 2 sides the same length
- no sides the same length
- 1 right angle
- 1 angle larger than a right angle
- all 3 angles smaller than a right angle

Part 4

Measure each side of the triangle you drew in Part 1 to the nearest $\frac{1}{4}$ inch.

side *AB* _____ in.   side *BC* _____ in.   side *CA* _____ in.

1. Draw a ray, $\overrightarrow{AT}$. Draw a line segment, $\overline{BY}$. Draw a line, $\overleftrightarrow{ME}$.

• A   • T

• B   • Y

• M   • E

SRB
88 89

2. In the number 34.972

the 9 means ___0.9___

the 7 means _____

the 3 means _____

the 4 means _____

the 2 means _____

SRB
35

3. The turn of the angle is

○ less than a $\frac{1}{2}$ turn.

○ less than a $\frac{1}{4}$ turn.

○ greater than a $\frac{1}{2}$ turn.

○ a full turn.

SRB
149 150

4. Double these numbers: Triple these numbers:

6 → _____   4 → _____

8 → _____   6 → _____

12 → _____   11 → _____

5. Write the time in hours and minutes.

half-past 6 _____:_____

quarter-past 9 _____:_____

quarter to 12 _____:_____

10 minutes to 10 _____:_____

6. What temperature is it? _____

How many degrees difference is there between 90°F and the above temperature?

_____

SRB
152–154

°F
50
40
30
20
10

Quadrangle Explorations

Part 1 Follow these steps:

1. Mark four points on the circle.

2. Label the points *A, B, C,* and *D.*

3. Use a straightedge to connect pairs of
   points to form a quadrangle.

Part 2 Write all eight 4-letter names that are possible for your
quadrangle. The first letter of each name is given below.

| A _____ | A _____ | B _____ | B _____ |
| C _____ | C _____ | D _____ | D _____ |

Part 3 Work with a group.

Make quadrangles with straws and twist-ties. Make at least one of
each of the following kinds of quadrangles:

- all 4 sides equal in length
- 2 pairs of equal-length sides, but opposite sides not equal length
- 2 pairs of equal-length opposite sides
- only 2 parallel opposite sides, each a different length
- only 1 pair of equal-length opposite sides

Part 4 Measure each side of the quadrangle you drew in Part 1
to the nearest $\frac{1}{4}$ inch.

side *AB* _____ in.   side *BC* _____ in.   side *CD* _____ in.   side *DA* _____ in.

Estimate: The perimeter of my quadrangle is about _____ inches.

Math Boxes 6.5

1. Circle the lines that intersect.

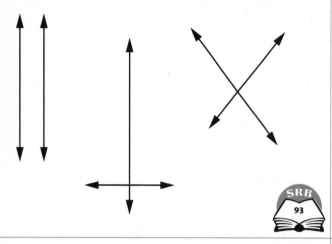

SRB
93

2. Circle the right angle.

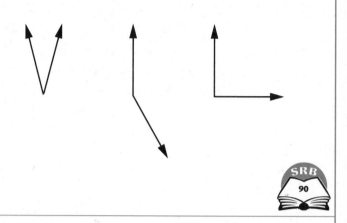

SRB
90

3. Write <, >, or =.

10 × 0 _____ 429 × 0

7 × 6 _____ 6 × 6

5 × 4 _____ 4 × 5

1 × 18 _____ 4 × 4

SRB
13
46 47

4. Measure each side of the triangle to the nearest centimeter.

_____ cm

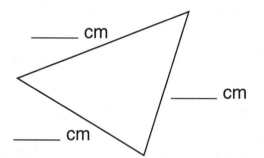

_____ cm

_____ cm

Perimeter = _____ cm

SRB
119–121
132 133

5. Complete the bar graph.

Lily ran 4 miles.

Meg ran 3 miles.

Rita ran 6 miles.

Median miles run: _____

SRB
80 81

6. Which is more?

1.36 or 1.6 _____

0.4 or 0.372 _____

0.69 or 0.6 _____

0.7 or 0.09 _____

SRB
36

Polygon Explorations

Part 1 Follow these steps:

1. Mark 5 points on the circle.

2. Label the points *A, B, C, D,* and *E.*

3. Use a straightedge to connect pairs
    of points to form a polygon.

4. What kind of polygon is it? _____

5. Write 4 or more possible names for your polygon.

    _____   _____   _____

    _____   _____   _____

Part 2 Work with a group.

Make polygons with straws and twist-ties. Your teacher will tell you
how many sides your polygons should have.

Make at least one of each of the following kinds of polygons:

*   all sides equal in length, and all angles equal in size (the amount of turn
    between sides)

*   all sides equal in length, but not all angles equal in size

*   *any* polygon having the assigned number of sides

Polygon Explorations (cont.)

Part 3 A **regular polygon** is a polygon in which all the sides are equal and all the angles are equal.

Below, trace the smaller of each kind of *regular* polygon from your Pattern-Block Template.

Below, trace all the polygons from your Pattern-Block Template that are *not* regular polygons.

Part 4 Measure each side of the polygon you drew in Part 1 to the nearest $\frac{1}{2}$ centimeter.

side *AB* _____ cm

side *BC* _____ cm

side *CD* _____ cm

side *DE* _____ cm

side *EA* _____ cm

Estimate: The perimeter of my polygon is about _____ cm.

Use with Lesson 6.6.

Math Boxes 6.6

1. Draw a ray, $\overrightarrow{SO}$. Draw a line segment, $\overline{LA}$. Draw a line, $\overleftrightarrow{TI}$.

•   •

•   •

•   •

SRB
88 89

2. Fill in the missing numbers. Add going across and subtract going down.

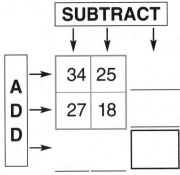

3. The turn of the angle is

○ greater than a $\frac{1}{4}$ turn.

○ less than a $\frac{1}{4}$ turn.

○ greater than a $\frac{1}{2}$ turn.

○ a full turn.

SRB
149 150

4. 9 boxes of muffins. 6 muffins per box. How many muffins in all?

_____ muffins

Write a number model:

_____ × _____ = _____

SRB
191 192

5. Draw a shape with 4 sides that are all equal in length.

This shape is a _____.

SRB
98 99

6. Complete the Fact Triangle. Write the fact family.

_____

_____

_____

_____

SRB
48 49

Drawing Angles

Draw each angle as directed by your teacher.
Record the direction of each turn with a curved arrow.

Part 1

A •   B •   C •

Part 2

R •   S •   T •

Use with Lesson 6.7.

1. Label all the points of these intersecting lines. Name the 2 lines.

_____

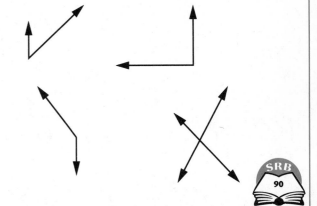

2. Circle the regular polygons.

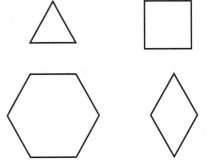

SRB
94 95

---

3. Fill in the unit box. Then divide.

Unit

$25 \div 5 = $ _____

$18 \div 3 = $ _____

_____ $= 30 \div 5$

$28 \div 7 = $ _____

_____ $= 24 \div 4$

SRB
46 47

4. Circle the right angle.

SRB
90

---

5. Measure each side of the triangle to the nearest centimeter.

_____ cm

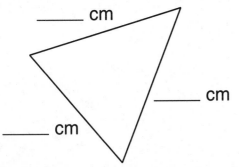

_____ cm

_____ cm

Perimeter = _____ cm

SRB
119–121

6. In the number 4.908

the 4 means ___*4 ones*___

the 0 means _____

the 9 means _____

the 8 means _____

SRB
35

Marking Angle Measures

Connect 2 straws with a twist-tie. Bend the twist-tie at the connection.

Place the straws on the circle.

- Place the bend on the center of the circle.
- Place both straws pointing to 0°.

Keep one straw pointing to 0°. Move the other straw to form angles.

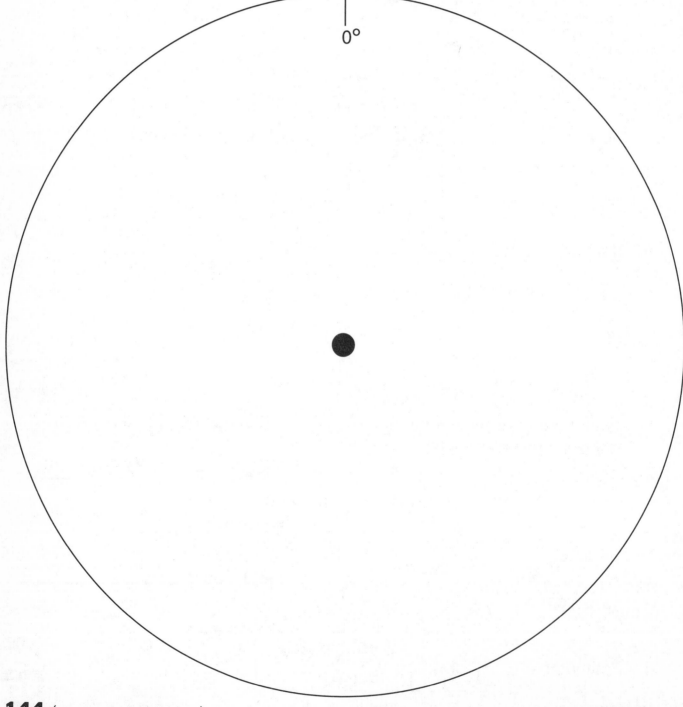

0°

Use with Lesson 6.8.

Measuring Angles

Use your angle measurer to measure the angles on this page.
Record your measurements in the table.

Angle	Measurement
A	about _____°
B	about _____°
C	between _____° and _____°
D	about _____°
E	about _____°
F	about _____°

Math Boxes 6.8

1. Draw a ray, $\overrightarrow{DO}$. Draw a line segment, $\overline{RE}$. Draw a line, $\overleftrightarrow{MI}$.

•   •

•   •

•   •

SRB 88 89

2. Complete the equal-sharing story.

14 _____ are shared equally

by _____ girls.

How many _____ does each

_____ get? _____

How many _____ are

left over? _____

SRB 191 192

3. The turn of the angle is

◯ greater than a $\frac{3}{4}$ turn.

◯ less than a $\frac{1}{4}$ turn.

◯ greater than a $\frac{1}{2}$ turn.

◯ a full turn.

SRB 149 150

4.
Double these numbers:	Triple these numbers:
15 → _____	10 → _____
80 → _____	25 → _____
200 → _____	300 → _____

5. Draw a quadrangle with exactly one right angle.

SRB 98 99

6. Complete the number-grid puzzle.

2,014

Symmetric Shapes

Each picture below shows one half of a letter. The dashed line is the line of symmetry. Guess what the letter is. Then draw the other half of the letter.

1.
2.
3.
4.

Draw the other half of each symmetric shape below.

5.   6.

7.   8.

9. The picture at the right shows one-fourth of a symmetric shape. There are two lines of symmetry. Draw the mirror image for each line of symmetry.

Challenge

10. There are 2 more lines of symmetry in Problem 9. Draw them.

Math Boxes 6.9

1. Draw a line segment, $\overline{DI}$, parallel to the line, $\overleftrightarrow{PO}$. Draw a ray, $\overrightarrow{LA}$, that intersects the line, $\overleftrightarrow{TW}$.

P   O

T   W

SRB 88 91

2. Describe a regular polygon.

_____

_____

_____

_____

_____

SRB 94 95

3. Fill in the unit box. Then multiply.

Unit

$4 \times 5 =$ _____

$7 \times 3 =$ _____

_____ $= 4 \times 4$

_____ $= 5 \times 3$

_____ $= 7 \times 5$

SRB 46 47

4. The degree measure of the angle is

○ more than 90°.

○ less than 90°.

○ more than 180°.

○ 120°.

SRB 149 150

5. Measure each side of the quadrangle to the nearest half-centimeter.

_____ cm

_____ cm   _____ cm

_____ cm

Another name for this quadrangle

is a _____.

SRB 99 119–121

6. Circle the right angle.

SRB 90

Math Boxes 6.10

1. These letters are *Symmets*:

H, T, M, A

This letters are not *Symmets*:

F, J, R, S

Write other letters that are *Symmets*:

_____

SRB
111 112

2. Write the number that has

7 in the thousandths place

5 in the ones place

1 in the tenths place

3 in the hundredths place

__ . __ __ __

SRB
35

3. The turn of the angle is

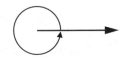

$\bigcirc$ a $\frac{1}{4}$ turn.

$\bigcirc$ less than a $\frac{1}{4}$ turn.

$\bigcirc$ less than a $\frac{1}{2}$ turn.

$\bigcirc$ a full turn.

SRB
149 150

4. Read the graph.

Days of Rain

Which month had the most days of rain?

_____

What is the median number of days of rain? _____

SRB
82 83

5. Draw a quadrangle with exactly one pair of parallel sides.

This shape is called a

_____.

SRB
99

6. Draw a 4-by-8 array of Xs.

How many Xs in all? _____
Write a number model.

_____

SRB
63 64

Base-10 Block Decimal Designs

Materials
- ❑ base-10 blocks (cubes, longs, and flats)
- ❑ 10-by-10 grids (*Math Journal 1,* p. 151)
- ❑ crayons or colored pencils

Think of the *flat* as a unit, or ONE. Remind yourself of the answers to the following questions:

- How many cubes would you need to cover the whole flat?

- How much of the flat is covered by 1 cube? By 1 long?

Follow these steps:

Step 1 Make a design by putting some cubes on a flat.

Step 2 Copy your design in color onto one of the grids on journal page 151.

Step 3 How much of the flat is covered by the cubes in your design? To help you find out, exchange as many cubes as you can for longs.

Step 4 Figure out which decimal tells how much of the flat is covered by cubes. Write the decimal under the grid that has your design on it.

Example

Steps 1 and 2: Make a design on a flat with cubes. Copy the design onto a grid.

Step 3: Exchange cubes for longs. Figure out how much of the flat is covered.

Step 4: Write the decimal under the grid.

Make other designs with cubes on flats, and draw them on the grids. Write a decimal for each design.

Decimal: 0.24

10 × 10 Grids

Decimal: _____

Decimal: _____

Decimal: _____

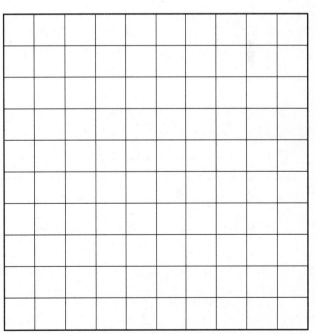

Decimal: _____

Symmetry

If a shape can be folded in half so that the two halves match exactly, the shape is **symmetric.** We also say that the shape has **symmetry.**

The fold line is called the **line of symmetry.** Some symmetric shapes have just one line of symmetry. Others have more.

1 line of symmetry

2 lines of symmetry

3 lines of symmetry

---

1. Which of the following shapes is **not** symmetric? _____

    a.

    b.

    c.

    d.

    e.

    f.

    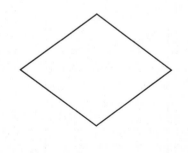

2. Draw all the lines of symmetry on the shapes that are symmetric.

Use with Lesson 6.11.

Math Boxes 6.11

1. If a map scale shows that $\frac{1}{2}$ inch represents 50 miles, then

1 inch represents _____ miles

2 inches represents _____ miles

4 inches represents _____ miles

_____ inches represents 500 miles

SRB
164

2. Figure out this riddle:

I have four sides. My opposite sides are equal in length. One set of my sides is longer than the other set of my sides. What shape am I?

_____

SRB
98 99

3. Fill in the unit box. Then divide.

Unit

$12 \div 3 = $ _____

_____ $ = 25 \div 5$

_____ $ = 28 \div 4$

_____ $ = 21 \div 7$

$24 \div 4 = $ _____

SRB
46 47

4. The degree measure of the angle is

O more than 90°.

O less than 90°.

O more than 180°.

O 40°.

SRB
149 150

5. Measure the sides of the quadrangle to the nearest centimeter.

_____ cm

_____ cm

_____ cm

_____ cm

Another name for this quadrangle is

_____.

SRB
99
119–121

6. Draw the lines of symmetry.

There are _____ lines of symmetry.

SRB
111 112

Pattern-Block Prisms

Work in a group.

1. Each person chooses a different pattern-block shape.

2. Each person then stacks 3 or 4 of the shapes together.
   See below.

3. Each person makes a prism by using small pieces of tape to hold
   the blocks together.

4. Below, carefully trace around each face of your prism. Then trace
   around each face of 2 or 3 more prisms on a separate sheet of
   paper. Share prisms with other people in your group. Ask
   someone in your group for help if you need it.

Math Boxes 6.12

1. Name each 3-dimensional shape.

_____

_____

_____

SRB
105
107 108

2. Draw a line, $\overleftrightarrow{AB}$, parallel to line segment $\overline{CD}$. Draw a ray, $\overrightarrow{EF}$, that intersects ray $\overrightarrow{GH}$.

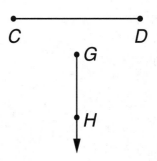

SRB
88 89
91

3. Give two reasons that this hexagon is not a regular hexagon.

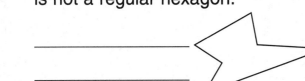

_____

_____

_____

_____

_____

SRB
95

4. The degree measure of the angle is

○ more than 120°.

○ less than 45°.

○ more than 180°.

○ 90°.

SRB
149 150

5. What is a quadrangle?

_____

_____

_____

_____

_____

_____

SRB
98

6. Trace a figure from your template and draw the lines of symmetry.

The figure is a _____.

SRB
95
111 112

It has _____ lines of symmetry.

Math Boxes 6.13

---

1. Solve.

$2 \times 2 = $ _____

$5 \times 5 = $ _____

_____ $= 3 \times 3$

_____ $= 4 \times 4$

---

2. Circle the even numbers.

23,406   129

700,001   44,444

57   135,790

The numbers that are not circled are called _____ numbers.

---

3. Solve.

$5 \times 4 = $ _____

$2 \times 7 = $ _____

_____ $= 3 \times 10$

_____ $= 7 \times 10$

$3 \times 5 = $ _____

---

4. Continue the pattern.

_____

---

5. Complete.

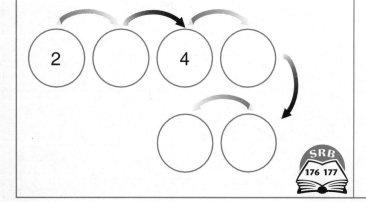

---

6. Write the fact family.

_____

_____

_____

_____

Special Pages

The following pages will be used throughout the school year, first in this journal and then again in your *Math Journal 2* later during the year.

	Page
Sunrise and Sunset Record	158
Length of Day	159
National High/Low Temperature Project	160

On the Sunrise and Sunset Record on journal page 158, you will record the date, and then the time of sunrise and the time of sunset for that date. You will begin to do this at the end of Unit 1 and then once a week or so whenever your teacher tells you.

Then later in the year, you will use the data that you have recorded on journal page 158 to make a graph on journal page 159. Your teacher will teach you how to do this in Unit 5.

Finally, on the National High/Low Temperature Project on journal page 160, you will record the following data: the U.S. city with the highest temperature and the U.S. city with the lowest temperature for the same date. You will do this every week or whenever your teacher tells you.

When you begin your *Math Journal 2* later in the school year, you will continue to record the sunrise and sunset times, and the highest and the lowest temperatures on pages in that journal. Near the end of the school year, you will use all this information.

Sunrise and Sunset Record

Date	Time of Sunrise	Time of Sunset	Length of Day	
			hr	min
			hr	min
			hr	min
			hr	min
			hr	min
			hr	min
			hr	min
			hr	min
			hr	min
			hr	min
			hr	min
			hr	min
			hr	min
			hr	min
			hr	min
			hr	min
			hr	min
			hr	min
			hr	min
			hr	min

Length of Day

National High/Low Temperatures Project

Date	Highest Temperature		Lowest Temperature		Difference in Temperature
	Place	Temperature	Place	Temperature	
		°F		°F	°F
		°F		°F	°F
		°F		°F	°F
		°F		°F	°F
		°F		°F	°F
		°F		°F	°F
		°F		°F	°F
		°F		°F	°F
		°F		°F	°F
		°F		°F	°F
		°F		°F	°F
		°F		°F	°F
		°F		°F	°F
		°F		°F	°F
		°F		°F	°F
		°F		°F	°F
		°F		°F	°F
		°F		°F	°F
		°F		°F	°F
		°F		°F	°F
		°F		°F	°F

Use with Lesson 2.6.

Paper Clock

1. Cut out the clock face, the minute hand, and the hour hand.

2. Punch a hole through the center of the clock face and through the Xs on the hands.

3. Fasten the hands to the clock face with a brad.

a brad

minute hand

hour hand

Rulers

Cut out the rulers.

Inches (in.)　　Ruler A

Inches (in.)　　Ruler B

Inches (in.)　　Ruler C

Inches (in.)　　Ruler D

Centimeters (cm)　　Ruler E

Multiplication/Division Fact Triangles 1

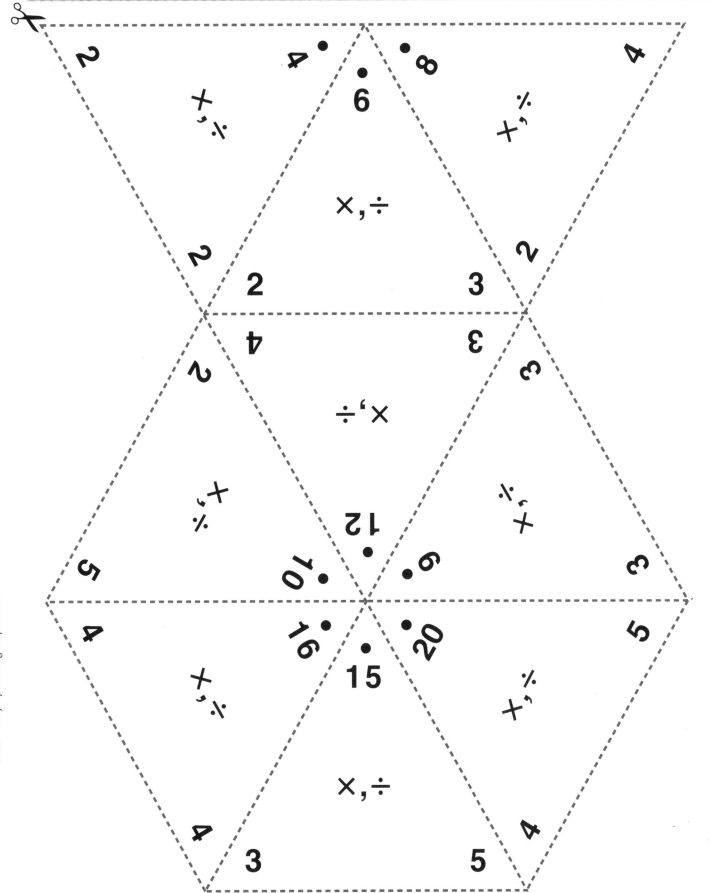

Use with Lesson 4.6.

Activity Sheet 3

Multiplication/Division Fact Triangles 2

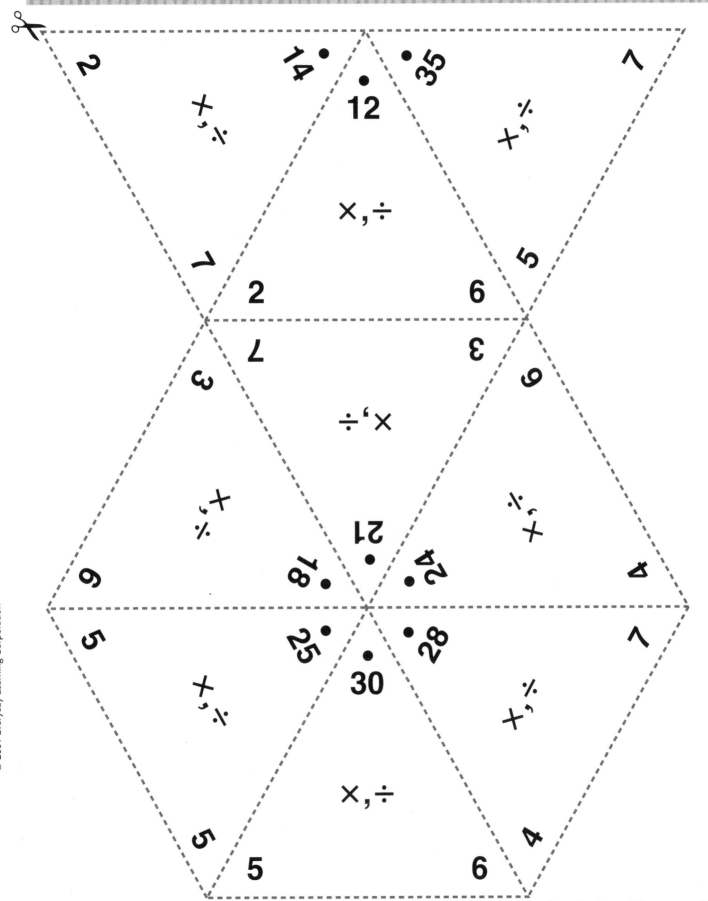

Use with Lesson 4.6.

Activity Sheet 4